SHELLS

GUIDE TO THE JEWELS OF THE SEA

WHITE STAR
PUBLISHERS

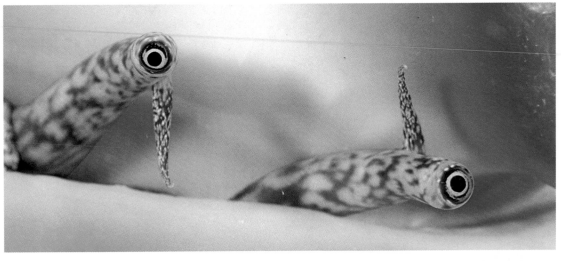

4 top The somewhat astonished-looking eyes of the strombid known as the "sea scorpion" (Lambis lambis).

4-5 Marine mollusks are masters of mimicry; the mollusk has made itself invisible by assuming the bright red color that other animals on the coral reef use to discourage predators, a signal that means their tissues contain stinging cells.

INTRODUCTION	page	6
A Resource for humanity	page	8
HOW A SHELL IS CREATED	page	12
A familiy tree 600 million years old	page	12
Questions of kinship	page	18
MOLLUSKS: ANATOMY OF A WINNER	page	28
In the belly of a marine snail	page	30
FEEDING, REPRODUCING, DEFENSE: THE VITAL FUNCTIONS	page	32
Movement	page	32
Respiration	page	36
The nervous system and sensory organs	page	37
Feeding	page	40
Reproduction	page	46
THE MOTHER-OF-PEARL FACTORY	page	54
WHERE SHELLS ARE FOUND	page	66
Geography of marine Mollusks	page	66
The salt water realms	page	74
On Coastal Rocks	page	78
Descent into the Shadows	page	84
On and Under the sand and mud	page	88
The coral theatre	page	92
Hidden in underwater meadows	page	98
The mangrove forests	page	104
From the high sea	page	108
HOW TO COLLECT SHELLS	page	112
THE SHELLS OF THE SEA	page	118

Cover
A cowrie in its mantle.
(© Jeff Rotman)

Back cover
top - Ovulidae on a coral.
(© Claudio Cangini)

center - Nautilus close to a gorgonian.
(© Andrea and Antonella Ferrari)

bottom - From left to right, the drawings show a Aporrhais pespelecani, a Cerithium nodulosum, and a Gibbula magus.
(© Monica Falcone)

1 The gastropodis foot permits all types of movement: through the mechanism of reptation, lifting, covering with sand, or climbing. The photo shows a small trochid in the process of climbing.

2-3 A giant clam from the Great Barrier Reef of Australia exposes its brightly colored mantle to the sunlight.

© 1999, 2000 White Star S.r.l.
Via Candido Sassone, 22-24
13100 Vercelli, Italy

Distributed in Egypt by
White Star Egypt
Luxor, Egypt

ISBN 88-8095-413-X

Printed in 2000 by
Rotolito Lombarda, Italy.

SHELLS

GUIDE TO THE JEWELS OF THE SEA

Text
Giorgio Gabbi

Editorial realization
Valeria Manferto De Fabianis
Laura Accomazzo

Graphic realization
Anna Galliani

Drawings
Monica Falcone

Translation
S.T.V., Milan

INTRODUCTION

Shells are beautiful, with elegant forms, surprising sculptures, refined designs and captivating colors. Shells remain intact for long periods of time, like precious metals and gems. And in fact, costly pearls are nothing more than a shell covering that the oyster builds around a foreign body that has entered its tissues. When man succeeded in producing that most noble of ceramic products, porcelain, he gave it the name of a shell, the cowry ("porcellana" in Italian), with its unparalleled glossy, smooth surface. And mother-of-pearl, an iridescent product from the humble abalone of our reefs, can provide an elegant touch to a simple button, and in its more precious forms provides the raw material for refined jewelry work.

Thus, it is no wonder that little shell treasures have been found with the remains of our most distant ancestors. It is yet another indication that the Paleolithic hunters and gatherers we commonly call cave men and women, had aesthetic tastes quite akin to our own, as we work and play at our computers. Archaeological excavations on sites that date back to classical antiquity have revealed collections of shells that came from thousands of kilometers away. In ancient Rome, they came from India, along with spices, gems, perfumes, and precious cloths. At the time of the great explorations, the dwellings of the rich and cultured of Europe were filled with spectacular, exotic shells. By that time, shell collecting was no longer just an aesthetic undertaking, but an homage to the first conquests of modern science.

Thus, without knowing it, the child who stoops to collect a shell on the seashore is repeating a gesture that human beings have performed since the dawn of the evolution of our species. And why is the eye irresistibly attracted to the form of a shell? Perhaps because, while it is a part of nature, it is different from anything else found in creation. Certainly, a worm or a curled-up caterpillar takes on a spiral form, but the result is banal and arouses no curiosity. The snail's spiral is something unique, different, and only in modern times has science discovered its secret: it is a logarithmic spiral, a line that runs according to a rigorous mathematical relationship. No wonder it tantalizes the eye and mind.

But many of us do not ask such difficult questions. More simply, shells bring the sea to our homes. They remind us of beautiful sunny days, the salt air and the enthusiasm we want to relive next year, perhaps on the same beach, or maybe in a completely different place - the tropics or the antipodes. For those who scuba dive, every shell evokes a particular seabed, the thrill of a new panorama discovered while exploring the blue depths. Even a simple bag of detritus, to be explored with a lens on a winter evening to reveal its little hidden treasures, takes us back to a magnificent, sheer wall, adorned with sea fans, or to a special grotto, dark as night but full of promise, or above the shining splendour of that coral formation, or into the green twilight of a forest of oarweed.

In this book, shells will be considered as travel companions, guides to exploring the marine environments that their makers, the mollusks, conquered well over 600 million years ago. To us, they will be much more than beautiful objects or alluring memories: they will help us understand and interpret the often enigmatic panoramas of the "sixth continent," which extends from the coastline where we feel the first sprays of water to the last horizon, where the blue of the sea merges with the sky. We will briefly consider the importance of mollusks and shells to man in both the past and the present, their unwitting role in the evolution of primitive society, and in trade, art, and science. Finally, we'll have some practical advice on producing a collection of shells that is beautiful to look at, helpful in understanding the sea, and respectful of nature.

6-7 The highly elegant spiral of a fossil mollusk, a pyrite ammonite from the genus Pleuroceras, found in Germany. It dates back to the Jurassic period (from 180 to 135 million years ago), when these cephalopods from the ammonoid subclass underwent their greatest expansion. Like present-day nautiluses (who are nevertheless not their descendants), they had a shell formed of chambers divided by septa.

A RESOURCE FOR HUMANITY

A - From prehistoric times to the present, most people on the planet, including those who live far from the sea, have used shells for jewelry. One of the necklaces the dancer in this photo is wearing is made of large cowry shells.

B - These little disks of mother-of-pearl and turquoise, used as earrings and clothing ornaments, look modern, but come from the Huan-Tihuanaco culture, which flourished in present-day Peru and Bolivia between the sixth and eleventh centuries.

A

Would our ancestors have survived without the protein supplied by the flesh of marine mollusks and the hard, sharp, easily worked material of their shells? Perhaps they would have, but prehistoric man's path would certainly have been more uncertain and difficult. Archaeologists have studied the enormous deposits of edible mollusk shells found along coasts throughout the world, from northern Europe to the most remote oceanic islands. Rather than the remains of gourmet shellfish banquets, they appear to be signs of a last ditch resource of hunters and gatherers who found it difficult to locate it other sources of food. Ancient Polynesian people did something unprecedented when they explored and colonized the immense Pacific Ocean, from Hawaii to the Easter Islands to New Zealand, using no navigational instruments as they crossed thousands of kilometers of open sea that separated one archipelago from another. They certainly would not have survived if they did not have the multiple resources of shells, but the ancient conquerors of the ocean transformed the nacre of the pearl oyster into the fish hook, the primary tool of a population of fishermen and navigators. By fishing along the way, one could travel across the open sea for weeks or even months.

Scrapers, knives, arrowheads, and hoe blades are only a few examples of the vital tools that our stone age ancestors knew how to make from shells. But since the dawn of humankind, the most beautiful and curious shells have been used not only for utilitarian purposes, but to satisfy spiritual needs. As early as the European Neolithic, it had been discovered that the trumpet shell *(Charonia tritonis),* with its truncated apex, could be used as a

musical instrument, a tradition that continued until classical antiquity. In Greece and Rome, a sea god, Triton, was depicted in the act of blowing the shell named after him. The people of pre-Columbian America used the shells of larger conches for the same purpose.

Universally used as amulets, symbols of authority, or ornaments to adorn belts, necklaces, hats and clothes, the shell has been traded among coastal and inland peoples since prehistoric times, and its two qualities, great durability and an easily recognizable form, transformed it from a trading object to a form of money. This probably took place in China as early as the second and first millennium before Christ, and lasted until metal money was introduced around 600 AD.

But the financial success of cowries in the moneta and annulus species, known as cowries from the term kavari that was used for them in South India, would last another 2500 years. In the mid 10th century, the Arabian writer Ma'Sudi wrote in his book about the Maldive Islands, The Golden Meadows: The queen knows no other money than the cowry. When her treasure diminishes, she orders the islanders to cut fronds of the coconut palm and throw them onto the water. The cowries climb on, are gathered and placed on the sandy shore, where the sun consumes them and leaves only the empty shells. And these are delivered to the treasury. Thousands and thousands of tons of these shells have traveled from archipelagos and the coasts of the Indian Ocean to sub-Saharan West Africa. During centuries of slave tradeing, cowries were abundantly used by slave traders; in 1522, the price of a slave in Benin was between 5460 and 6370 cowries.

Only at the end of the 19th century did colonial powers take cowries out of circulation as currency. Nevertheless, for the entire 20th century, they continued to be used as small change in village markets. Other shells that made history in international trade even in ancient times include the pearl oyster (from the genus *Pinctada*) and murices, which were used to extract the famous purple dye of the Phoenicians. Almost everywhere, pearls of varying beauty and regularity from a number of marine and fresh water families had been used to make ornaments, but only those taken from Pinctada, with a perfect form and high gloss, acquired extremely high value. They were part of temple and royal treasures, adorned the crowns of queens and emperors, and shone around the necks or on the fingers of a very select number of privileged ladies. Their value peaked in ancient Rome. In his Natural History, Pliny the Elder wrote that they were the most precious thing in the world, and the historian Svetonius wrote that Aulus Vitellius, Roman emperor in the year 69, paid for a military campaign with revenues from the sale of a single pearl earring inherited from his mother.

Pearl fishing, which some young Arabs from wealthy families in oil sheikdoms practice for sport, was centered in the

B

Persian Gulf, and the lives of pearl fishermen, who made free dives dozens of times a day, were extremely harsh. Disability and early death were quite common. Starting in the early 19th century, the button industry created great demand for mother-of-pearl, and pearl fishermen could thus enjoy a modest but secure living by gathering pearl oysters. Overharvesting meant finding a valuable pearl had become an increasingly remote possibility. The physiological mechanism that an oyster, a murex, a fan mussel, or a nautilus uses to produce a pearl was discovered. When a foreign body ends up in the mollusk's tissues, it reacts by wrapping it in concentric layers of mother-of-pearl and making a sort of appendage within the shell. In the late 19th century, three Japanese researchers independently discovered the secret of forcing an oyster to make a pearl to order, and one of the three, Kokichi Mikimoto, based a business empire on the discovery. The secret is a rather delicate surgical operation that transplants into the tissues of a pearl oyster raised in captivity, a mother-of-pearl nucleus wrapped in a flap of tissue capable of producing mother-of-pearl, taken from another oyster. Another family of mollusks that was the centre of a flourishing international trade in ancient times was the murices. Various people at various times have discovered and exploited the dyes in the mucus secreted by a gland located below the gills of murices, but only the Phoenicians were able to make it the basis of a flourishing industrial and commercial monopoly. Three species were utilized: the purple dye murex *(Bolinus brandaris)*, the red-mouth purpura *(Thais lacera)* and the trunculus murex *(Hexaplex trunculus)*: each mollusk produced only a few drops of a yellowish mucus which quickly turned dark blue when exposed to the light.

In Ireland, piles of broken shells of the murex *Nucella lapillus* have been found. One thousand years before Christ, the ancient Irish used them to obtain a black purple dye. Another luxury product provided by mollusks was taken from the byssus, the complex of filaments secreted by the glands of the foot and used by many species of bivalves to anchor to solid parts of the substratum. Processed and spun, the byssus takes on a silky texture.

Today, an increasing number of countries limits the collection of mollusks for commercial use and encourages their cultivation. Thus, in tropical countries, mother-of-pearl is obtained from species that have proved easy to cultivate, like the topshell *Trocus niloticus* and the pearl oyster.

In 1972, one of the world's most authoritative associations of specialists in the sector, Unitas Malacologica Europaea, recommended limiting the collection of live mollusks for both scientific and amateur purposes, to protect populations that in many cases were threatened by negative factors like marine pollution or destruction of coastal habitats. In the following years, various international conventions compiled lists of threatened species or mollusk populations. An increasing number of countries have adopted measures to protect the marine environment, including limits and in some cases absolute bans on collecting shells, selling them or taking them outside the country. A conscientious collector will in any case set clear ethical limits. You should consult specialized publications to find out which species are endangered, and always be sure to gather only very modest amounts. With this in mind, remember that, as illustrious scientists have noted, gathering shells for study or collection has never and could never endanger the survival of any species of mollusk. As one of the great malacologists of this century, the American R. Tucker Abbott, who passed away a few years ago, stated: "...there seems amog extreme conservationists a reluctance to encourage shell collecting as a science or as a worthwhile hobby... However, an analysis of the fate of molluscan populations around the world indicates that the major causes of their reduction in most areas is due to pollution, man's destruction or major alteration of natural habitats, excessive commercial fishing, and finally the natural vagaries of mother nature herself..."

Nearly all species of mollusks produce thousands, or even millions, of young (in constrast to the small litters of mammals and limited broods of birds)... What marine scientists and shell collectors may harvest in their lifetimes has an effect on the size of the population of marine mollusks comparable to the contribution of the sound made by a ping-pong ball dropping at the foot of the roaring Niagara Falls. (The Seashells of South East Asia, Editor Graham Bash, Singapore, page 13).

So don't feel guilty about collecting shells, but always show respect for life. Thus, always try to collect shells of mollusks that have died of natural causes; often they are in perfect condition. When your search has an impact on the environment, like turning over rocks and pulling algae from the seabed, use the greatest discretion, always put the rocks back in their original position, and take only a small part of the vegetation you're interested in. If you want to collect a living mollusk (which you must do if you want to examine its behavior in an aquarium or dissect it to study its anatomy), only a minimal fraction of the local population should be sacrificed, to avoid changing the biological equilibrium. And when you find a species that through the fault of humans, collectors or not, has become rare or very rare in a certain area, for example *Pinna nobilis* or *Patella ferruginea* in Italy, if you find no empty shells, be happy with some notes in your notebook and a photograph. It will be a trophy of which you can be doubly proud: you found a rarity and you let it live.

C

C - In this English gilded silver salt shaker from the Elizabethan era, the sculptor used a nautilus shell (Nautilus pompilius) to make the body of the fighting cock.

10 - 11 The green and blue of the mother-of-pearl of an abalone (Haliotis iris) from New Zealand are due to the mollusk's habit of feeding on brown algae.

9

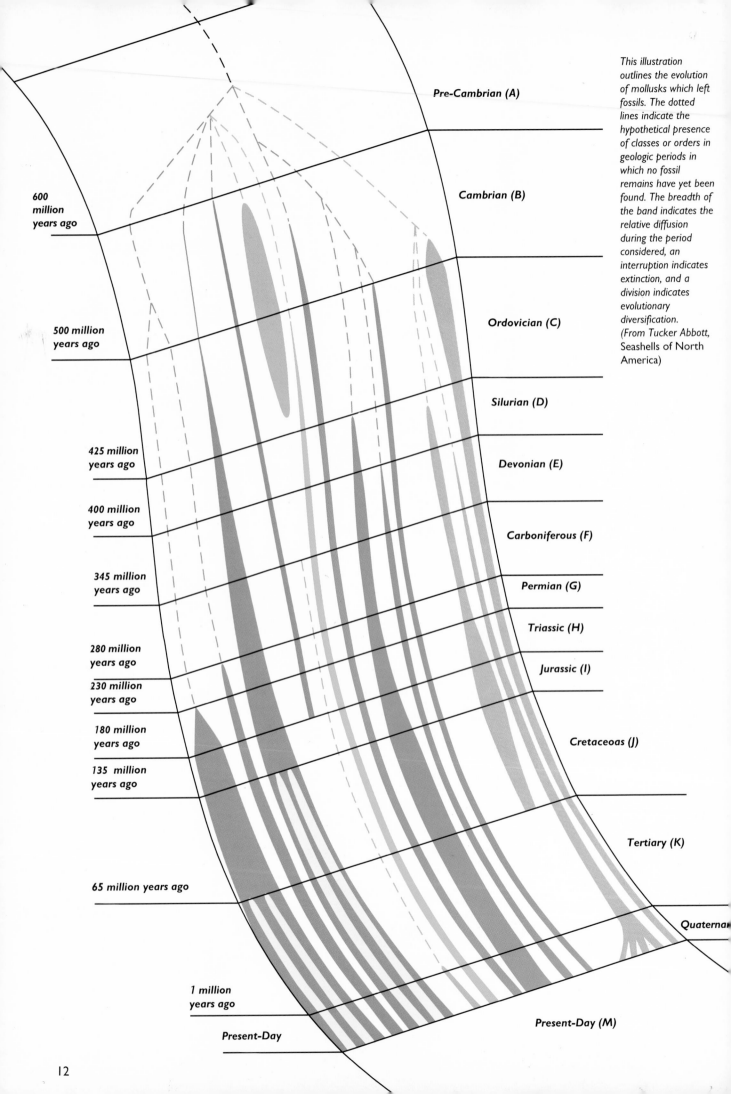

Pre-Cambrian (A)

Cambrian (B)

Ordovician (C)

Silurian (D)

Devonian (E)

Carboniferous (F)

Permian (G)

Triassic (H)

Jurassic (I)

Cretaceoas (J)

Tertiary (K)

Quaternar

Present-Day (M)

600 million years ago

500 million years ago

425 million years ago

400 million years ago

345 million years ago

280 million years ago

230 million years ago

180 million years ago

135 million years ago

65 million years ago

1 million years ago

Present-Day

This illustration outlines the evolution of mollusks which left fossils. The dotted lines indicate the hypothetical presence of classes or orders in geologic periods in which no fossil remains have yet been found. The breadth of the band indicates the relative diffusion during the period considered, an interruption indicates extinction, and a division indicates evolutionary diversification. (From Tucker Abbott, Seashells of North America)

*H*OW A SHELL IS CREATED

A FAMILY TREE 600 MILLION YEARS OLD

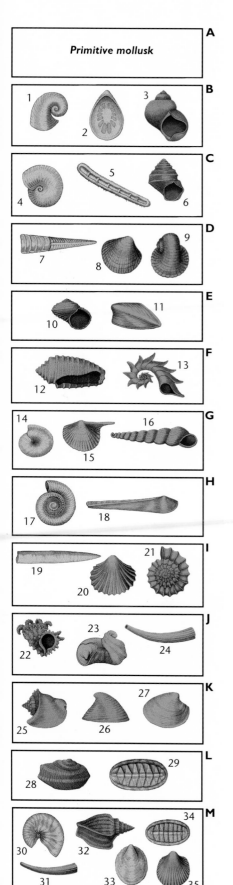

A	*Primitive mollusk*		

Gastropods

Monoplacophores

Amphineurans

Scaphodra

Bivalves

Cephalopods

A

Pre-Cambrian (A)

Cambrian (B)
1 *Bellerophonts*
2 *Monoplacophores*
3 *Prosobranchs*
Ordovician (C)
4 *Bellerophonts*
6 *Prosobranchs*
5 *Amphineurans*
Silurian (D)
8 *Bivalves*
7 *Nautiloids*
9 *Prosobranchs*
Devonian (E)
10 *Prosobranchs*
11 *Bivalves*
Carboniferous (F)
12 *Opisthobranchs*
13 *Prosobranchs*
Permian (G)
14 *Ammonites*
15 *Bivalves*
16 *Opisthobranchs*
Triassic (H)
17 *Ammonites*
18 *Bivalves*
Jurassic (I)
19 *Nautiloids*
20 *Bivalves*
21 *Ammonites*
Cretaceous (J)
22 *Prosobranchs*
23 *Bivalves*
24 *Scaphopods*

Tertiary (K)
25 *Prosobranchs*
26 *Prosobranchs*
27 *Bivalves*
Quaternary (L)
28 *Pulmonates*
29 *Amphineurans*
Present-Day (M)
30 *Cephalopods*
31 *Scaphopods*
32 *Gastropods*
33 *Monoplacophores*
34 *Amphineurans*
35 *Bivalves*

A - The outer imprint of an ammonite, found in Italy on Monte Nerone in the Marchigiano Apennines. Fossils of this cephalopod are particularly abundant in soil from the Jurassic and Triassic.

Finding marine fossil shells high up in the mountains, hundreds of kilometers from the sea, is always a cause for wonder. Our ancestors invented fantastic explanations for such a strange event, until Biblical tales set everyone straight by asserting that those petrified remains could be nothing other than traces of animal populations destroyed by the great flood - the antediluvians. To modern science, fossil shells were much more, and became an extraordinary aid to scholars in deciphering the earth's past. Geologists considered them the best fossil guides for dating sedimentary rocks, reconstructing climate changes in ancient seas, following the processes of land emergence and submersion, and many other kinds of research. Thanks to its calcareous hull, a shell leaves an always recognizable signature in the rock that imprisons it, even if the shell itself dissolves and comes to us only through the imprint of its interior.

The most ancient fossils date back to about 600 million years ago, the beginning of the Cambrian period, the earliest geologic period of the Paleozoic era. Before this period, scientists can only speculate as to how living beings evolved. In the Cambrian period, fossil mollusks already seem to have diversified into the classes that still survive today on the planet (the only one missing is the class of aplacophores, which has about 250 living species whose worm-like forms, with no shells, have left no fossils). The most remote finds, along with shells in surprising forms, show us snails and clams not very different from those of our days. Not to say that mollusks haven't evolved in a half a billion years - far from it. Entire large families have become extinct, and others which once dominated the seas have been reduced to just a few species. New families have emerged. But mollusks had already developed their fundamental anatomical structures even before fish and reptiles had appeared on the planet.

According to the most accredited hypothesis among scholars, the common ancestor of all mollusks was an organism with bilateral symmetry that had a shell with a depressed cone shape and moved by crawling on a fleshy foot. In outward appearance, at least, it was similar to present-day limpets (whose internal organization, however, is completely different). Of the six living classes of mollusks with a shell, the one considered most similar to this progenitor is the Monoplacophora class. This class had been considered extinct by the Paleozoic era when, on May 6, 1952, the Danish research vessel Galathea pulled up 13 specimens, three empty shells and ten living ones, from a clayey seabed west of Panama, at a depth of 5000 meters. For four years, these discoveries remained undisturbed in their glass bottles. Then, when malacologists Wingstrand and Lemche examined them, they realized that they were living fossils, practically identical to creatures that had been considered extinct for 400 million years. The discovery of Neopilina galatheae casts much light on the history of the first mollusks. Indeed, monoplacophores have at least a partially segmented body, a phenomenon known as metamerism. That is, they consist of parts (such as muscles, gills and kidneys) that appear in repeating pairs for each segment.

This structure begins to give us answers to some old questions: who are the mollusks' closest relatives? And who is their most remote ancestor? The organization of cuttlefish, snails, and mussels is so different from other invertebrates that any theory is hard to support. In the mid-18th century, the great Linnaeus (Carl von Linné, the Swedish scientist who in 1758 laid the foundations for natural systematics in the tenth edition of his work, *Sistema Naturae*), had placed mollusks among the Vermes, following a tradition that dated back to classical antiquity and was based on a superficial evaluation of external features, such as the softness of the body and the lack of well-defined limbs. Linnaeus' successors were quick to understand that there is

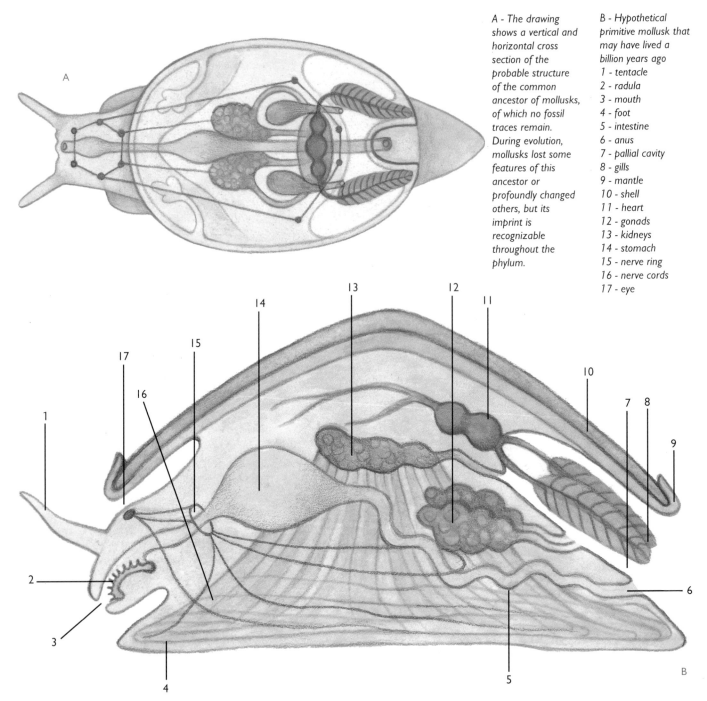

A - The drawing shows a vertical and horizontal cross section of the probable structure of the common ancestor of mollusks, of which no fossil traces remain. During evolution, mollusks lost some features of this ancestor or profoundly changed others, but its imprint is recognizable throughout the phylum.

B - Hypothetical primitive mollusk that may have lived a billion years ago
1 - tentacle
2 - radula
3 - mouth
4 - foot
5 - intestine
6 - anus
7 - pallial cavity
8 - gills
9 - mantle
10 - shell
11 - heart
12 - gonads
13 - kidneys
14 - stomach
15 - nerve ring
16 - nerve cords
17 - eye

formation of subspecies or even geographical races. Zoologists who study mollusks have always had significant differences of opinion on the validity of species and subspecies. In the past, when solely the external features of the shell were used to classify mollusks, an endless number of species was created, but this later proved to be inconsistent. Many species were attributed to genera or even families that were different from the original ones. In the meantime, many new species were found in nature. For someone who is not a professional zoologist, this makes it extremely difficult to consult texts that are more than fifteen or twenty years old. Anyone who is just beginning to collect shells should resign himself to the problem of nomenclature. With a bit of experience, you'll learn how to wade through old names, new names and eliminated names. In the end, what counts is not so much the name, but the bit of natural history that lies behind it.

C - This precious lithograph printed in Stuttgart in 1861 for the Systematische Atlas der Naturgeschichte (Systematic Atlas of Natural History) by T. Bromme presents characteristic shells from some of the most common families of bivalves.

D - The Swedish scientist Carl von Linné, in his catalogue of nature, Sistema Naturae, had placed molluscs under "Vermes".

as much difference between a snail and a leech as between a starfish and a poodle. Mollusks were then given their own group.

Modern science classifies living organisms based on their evolutionary history, i.e. their family tree. Within the animal kingdom, the organisms that have the same fundamental organization form a *phylum* (or type). *Phyla* (or types) include those of the mollusks, echinoderms, arthropods, and chordates. Within a phylum, organisms with a common ascendant are grouped into classes (for example, the phylum of chordates includes the classes of *Mammalia, Reptilia, Aves,* and so forth). Within each class, animals are grouped into orders (mammals, for example, include the orders of Carnivora, Rodentia, Insectivora, and so forth). Within each order, there are families (Carnivora is divided into *Canidae, Felidae, Ursidae,* and so on). Below the family, animals are classified

into genus (for example, the *Canidae* family includes the genera *Canis* and *Vulpes*) and the genera are divided into species (the genus *Canis* includes the species lupus, the wolf; aureus, the jackal; and familiaris, the domestic dog, while the genus *Vulpes* includes the species vulpes, the red fox; and chama, the African fox). We have used the example of mammals, which are the most familiar, to underline that, when we see two clams that look identical but have a different genus, they are actually as far apart on the family tree as a dog and a fox.

In zoology, the species is the fundamental group. Generally speaking, it indicates individuals that have a genetic heritage in common and can reproduce, generating fertile offspring. Particular environmental situations (such as isolation) can cause populations of the same species to have certain features that differentiate with regularity: we then speak of the

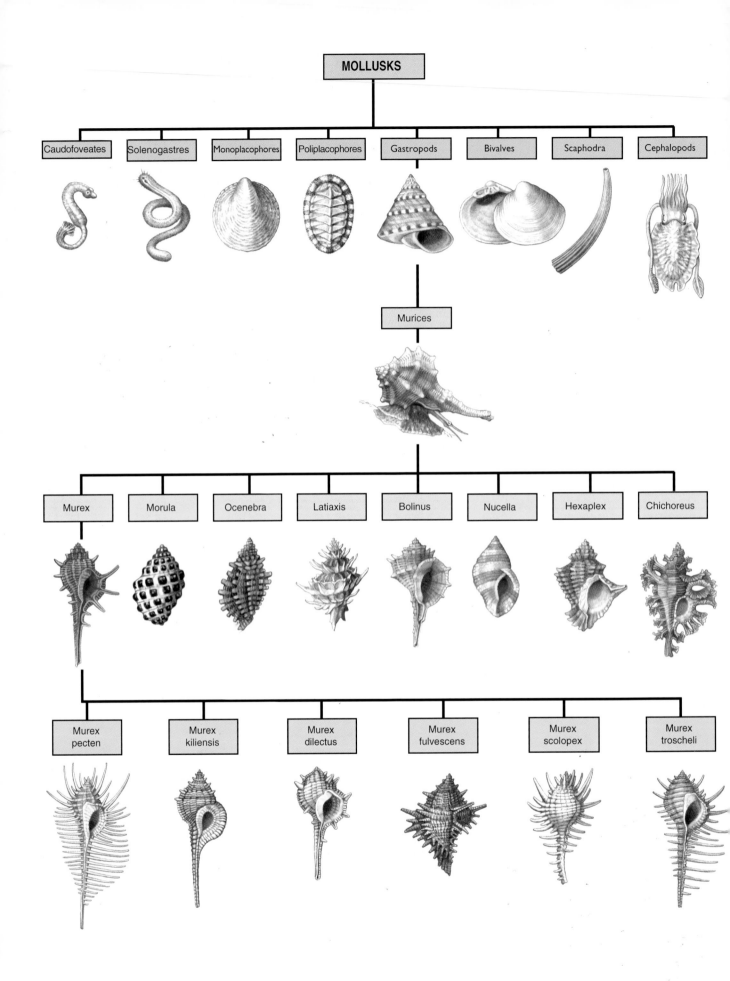

MOLLUSKS

Caudofoveates · Solenogastres · Monoplacophores · Poliplacophores · Gastropods · Bivalves · Scaphodra · Cephalopods

Murices

Murex · Morula · Ocenebra · Latiaxis · Bolinus · Nucella · Hexaplex · Chichoreus

Murex pecten · Murex kiliensis · Murex dilectus · Murex fulvescens · Murex scolopex · Murex troscheli

QUESTIONS OF KINSHIP

A, B and C - Considered to be living fossils, present-day monoplacophores have very primitive characteristics. In the drawing, a Neopilinia seen from above (A), from the side (B) and from the central area (C). The five pairs of gills could indicate that it is a descendant of a metameric ancestor, i.e. with a segmented body like that of anellids.

D, E, F and G - The drawings show a chiton (polyplacophore) as seen from above (D) and ventrally (E), as well as the scheme of its internal structure seen from the side (F) and the ventral portion (G). The shell,

1 - mouth
2 - shell
3 - foot
4 - mantle margin
5 - gills
6 - anus

divided into eight imbricate plates (13), allows it to adhere firmly to rocky surfaces.

1 - mouth
2 - head
3 - girdle
4 - gills
5 - intestine
6 - gonads
7 - excretory canals
8 - kidney
9 - heart
10 - anus
11 - radula
12 - foot
13 - shell with plates

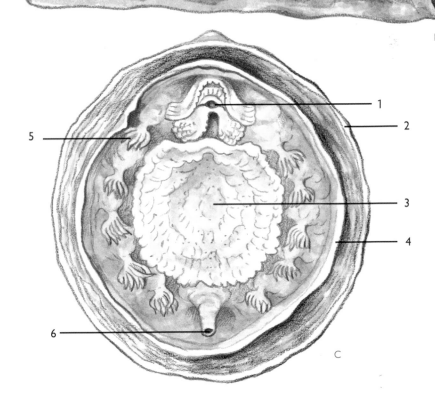

Getting back to the *phylum* of mollusks and the problem of what could be their progenitor, monoplacophore metamerism, even if only partial, provides a first indicator. Two other *phyla,* the arthropods and the anellids, are characterized by metamerism. The larval forms of species in these phyla have significant similarities. The same hint of metamerism present in polyplacaphores (see opposite) adds credence to this approach. Thus, the most accredited hypothesis today considers butterflies, earthworms and snails as possible descendants of a common, albeit very distant, progenitor.

Let us now look at kinship issues within the phylum of mollusks with a shell, i.e. the path their evolution took and the classes it originated.

MONOPLACOPHORES

After the sensational find of Neopilina galatheae, in the second half of the 20th century, another dozen species of these living fossils were found. They all live on seabeds, from depths of a few hundred meters to the abyss. They are all microphage detritovores. Their shells reaches a few centimeters in length.

H and I - In the drawing, a tusk shell, scaphopod, (H) and a cross-section (I) showing its internal structure. The animal is sedentary and lives attached to the bottom.

It feeds on detritus captured with its captacula, which also serve as gills. It has no eyes, and its nervous system is rudimentary.

1 - captacula
2 - foot
3 - mouth
4 - mantle
5 - nerve ganglia
6 - heart
7 - stomach

8 - kidney
9 - hepatopancreas
10 - gonads
11 - mantle cavity
12 - anus
13 - back aperture
14 - shellposteriore

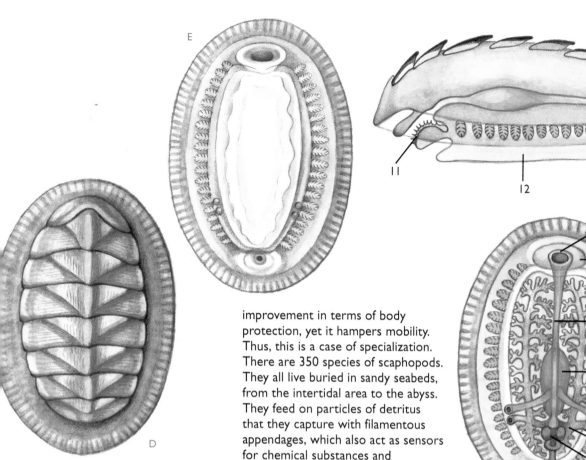

POLYPLACOPHORES

These are known as chitons, and it's not difficult to find them a few centimeters below the water surface on reefs in intertidal areas, adhering to substrata like limpets. Their shell is formed of eight plates, usually imbricate, i.e. overlapping like the tiles of a roof. Compared with the single shell of primitive mollusks, this transformation makes it much easier to adhere to the surface of a rock. The shell is permeated with pores, through which pass nerve endings with small sensory organs at the tips, both tactile and visual. This feature is similar to certain aspects of anellid anatomy. A maximum of thirty centimeters long, today there are about 600 living species of polyplacophores. They are herbivores and detritovores, and live anchored to the seabed, from intertidal areas to the abyss.

SCAPHOPODS

On sandy beaches you may find small, slightly arcuate, white tubes that somewhat resemble an elephant's tusk. These are tusk shells, members of the class of scaphopods. The transformation of the cone-shaped shell of primitive mollusks into a little tube seems to be a clear evolutionary improvement in terms of body protection, yet it hampers mobility. Thus, this is a case of specialization. There are 350 species of scaphopods. They all live buried in sandy seabeds, from the intertidal area to the abyss. They feed on particles of detritus that they capture with filamentous appendages, which also act as sensors for chemical substances and respiratory organs. Scaphopods do not exceed 12 centimeters in length, and have no head, eyes, or gills. The digestive tract and nervous system are rudimentary. Their sedentary existence under the layer of sand on the seabed and the type of food they eat have made it unnecessary to develop the organs and functions required of animals just slightly more active.

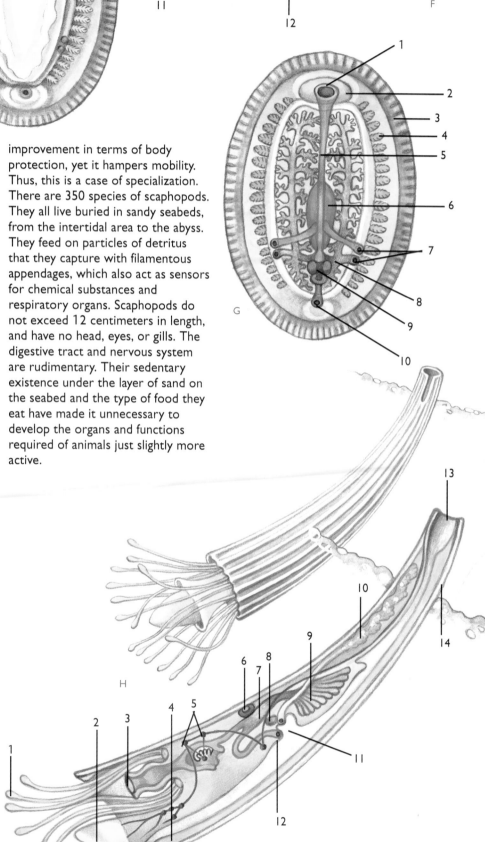

CEPHALOPODS

On the other hand, cephalopods, the most evolved of the mollusks, are quite active. They are all carnivorous. They live in the open sea, as a part of the nekton or benthos. In this class of mollusks, the shell may appear as an outer hull, coiled around a single plane, with the inside divided into watertight compartments, like the nautilus. Much more frequently, the shell is internal, and may be a calcareous substance like cuttlebone, or a horny one like the squid's pen. But it may be completely absent, as in the octopus. There are about 600 living species of cephalopods. With the giant squid, they reach record lengths of 12 meters.

A

B

C

A - The octopus is a cephalopod completely lacking a shell, even an internal one. The example pictured in the photo is "walking" on the bottom, using its eight tentacles equipped with suckers. When it has to move more quickly, the octopus activates its "jet propulsion engine" by expelling an energetic jet of water from the siphon. Both the siphon and tentacles are evolutionary developments of the foot of the primitive mollusk.

B - The drawing shows the structure of a cephalopod from the subclass of coleoids, which includes decapods (spirulae, cuttlefish and squid) and octopods (octopuses and argonauts). The pallial cavity (12) has become an organ for jet propulsion, regulated by the opening of the siphon (15).

1 - tentacle arm
2 - oral arm
3 - sucker
4 - mouth
5 - eye
6 - esophagus
7 - hepatopancreas
8 - heart
9 - gonads
10 - internal shell
11 - ink sac
12 - pallial cavity
13 - gills
14 - kidney
15 - siphon
16 - genital aperture
17 - excretory aperture
18 - anus
19 - cerebral ganglion

D

E - Internal structure of a nautilus. The spiral-shaped, symmetrical shell coiled around a single plane is divided into chambers (10) that the animal closes with a calcareous diaphragm (11) and abandons as it grows. The chambers connect to each other by means of a canal through which the nautilus pumps gas to modify its specific weight and move vertically.

1 - tentacles
2 - siphon
3 - mouth
4 - pallial cavity
5 - gills
6 - heart
7 - intestine
8 - shell
9 - canal
10 - chambers
11 - septa

G - A female Argonauta nodosa from southern Australia. In this genus of cephalopods, the male is much smaller than the female. The female builds a false shell (ootheca, or egg case) in which it keeps the eggs.

E

C - This long-fin squid (Loligo pealei) lives in the Northwest Atlantic. The largest member of the mollusk phylum is the giant squid, which can reach 12 meters in length.

D, F - The nautilus is a genus of cephalopods. It is a living fossil, the only representative that has survived of the subclass of nautiloids, which disappeared in the Paleozoic. Nautiloids were quite common and were sometimes gigantic; one fossil found in Germany was 2.4 meters in diameter. Nautiluses are pelagic, and feed on crustaceans.

F

G

A - The structure of the body of a bivalve in the Veneridae family (clams) as it appears with its valves open.

1 - foot
2 - mantle
3 - gills
4 - siphons
5 - shell

B - The drawing shows the structure of internal organs of a bivalve (Veneridae, clams) in a longitudinal cross-section.

1 - adductor muscles
2 - mouth
3 - foot
4 - visceral nerve ganglion
5 - intestine
6 - gonads
7 - gills
8 - pallial cavity
9 - siphons
10 - foot nerve ganglion
11 - anus
12 - kidney
13 - heart
14 - pericardium
15 - hepatopancreas
16 - stomach

BIVALVES

This class of mollusks has solved the problem of fully protecting its body by dividing its ancestral shell in two, creating two hinged plates, the valves. It is believed that this process took place in the Cambrian or Ordovician, when a monoplacophore evolved to adapt to life in a sandy environment. To better move through the grains of sand, the mollusk adopted a laterally compressed body form. The conical shell would have divided in two, as still occurs in the larval forms of bivalves, which have only one embryonal shell. The mollusk half-closes the valves to filter water and feed on the tiny organic particles in suspension, and to replenish its oxygen supply through the gills. Bivalves are animals that engage in little or no movement, as adults. This sedentary nature has had important consequences on their evolution. Among other things, it has led to the disappearance of a head and true eyes. Unlike the classes discussed above, bivalves have successfully ventured beyond the marine environment, populating rivers, lakes, ponds and streams. This class contains no fewer than 10,000 species, mostly marine and the rest freshwater. The largest bivalve, the giant clam, reaches 137 centimeters in length.

C - The drawing shows a cross section of the structure of a bivalve from the eulamellibranch order (clams, tellins, cockles), in particular the respiratory and circulatory system.
1 - heart
2 - blood vessels
3 - gills
4 - mantle
5 - shell
6 - pallial cavity
7 - foot

D - The drawing shows the phases of natural pearl formation in a bivalve. A: an irritating foreign object comes between the shell (1) and the epithelium of the mantle (2); the mollusk reacts by enveloping the foreign object with its mantle; the cells begin to secrete a thin layer of mother-of-pearl. Other layers are deposited (C and D) until a round pearl is formed.

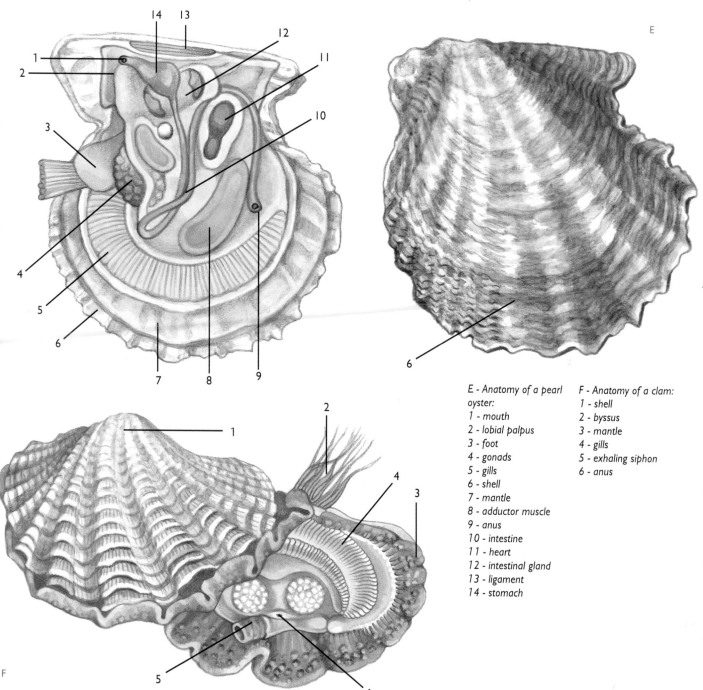

E - Anatomy of a pearl oyster:
1 - mouth
2 - lobial palpus
3 - foot
4 - gonads
5 - gills
6 - shell
7 - mantle
8 - adductor muscle
9 - anus
10 - intestine
11 - heart
12 - intestinal gland
13 - ligament
14 - stomach

F - Anatomy of a clam:
1 - shell
2 - byssus
3 - mantle
4 - gills
5 - exhaling siphon
6 - anus

GASTROPODS

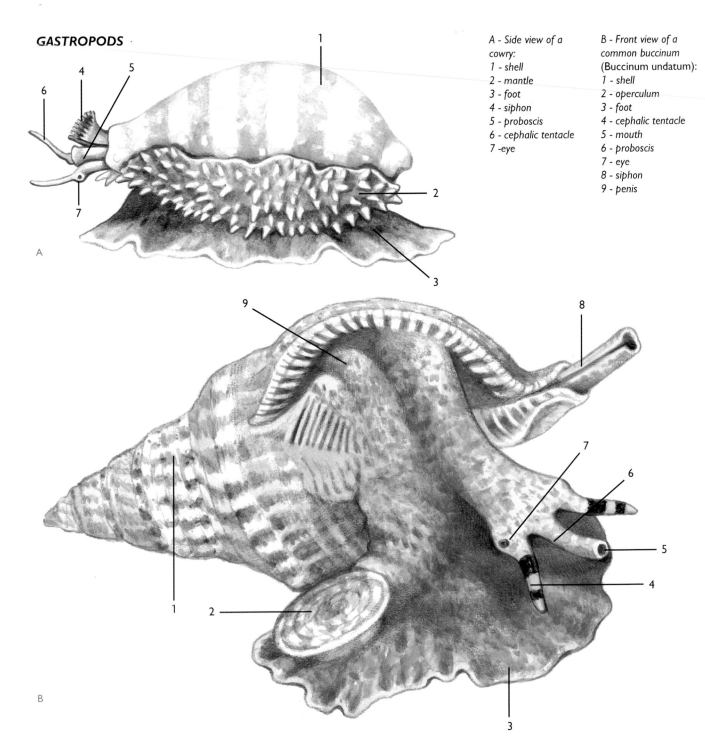

A - Side view of a cowry:
1 - shell
2 - mantle
3 - foot
4 - siphon
5 - proboscis
6 - cephalic tentacle
7 - eye

B - Front view of a common buccinum (Buccinum undatum):
1 - shell
2 - operculum
3 - foot
4 - cephalic tentacle
5 - mouth
6 - proboscis
7 - eye
8 - siphon
9 - penis

With the class of gastropods, mollusks conquered all environments on the planet - and the avid attention of collectors. Indeed, no other class of mollusks has such a wealth of species (more than 30,000) and shells prized for their beautiful forms, ornamentation and color. After occupying every ecological niche, from the coastline to the open sea to the abyss, gastropods colonized the fresh water (surface, underground and even thermal areas), and finally extended to dry land, from tropical forests to deserts and the high mountains. They stopped only at lands permanently covered with ice. Compared with the hypothetical primitive mollusk, the evolution of gastropods is marked by two fundamental developments: the first is the transformation of the shell from a shield to a spiral structure, i.e. a tube that gradually widens, coiling around an axis, and the second was the 180 degree counterclockwise torsion on a horizontal plane, of the mollusk's visceral mass. As the shell evolved, the shield of the primitive mollusk that was the gastropod's ancestor probably grew in height until it assumed a pointed cone form, offering more volume and thus better protection, as the mollusk could retract its entire body inside it, leaving exposed only the part

C - The anatomy of a common buccinum (Buccinum undatum) seen as if the shell and foot were transparent:

1 - head
2 - eye
3 - siphon
4 - blood vessels
5 - columellar muscle
6 - heart
7 - mucus gland
8 - gill
9 - osphradium
10 - cephalic tentacle

D - This Lambis was photographed in Polynesia as it cautiously advanced, exploring the environment with its primitive eyes. The long digitations of the shells of this genus make the animal quite stable even on loose surfaces.

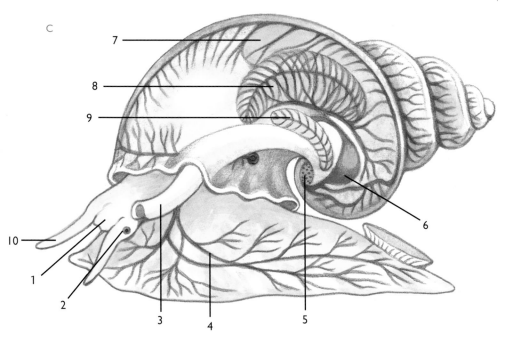

C

7
8
9
10
1
2
3
4
5
6

F

G

D

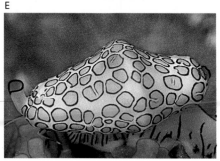

E

E - The spotted mantle of this ovulid from the Caribbean covers the shell entirely, as is common in families related to the cowries. Locally known as the flamingo tongue, Cyphoma gibbosum can reach 2.5 centimeters in length and prefers to live on gorgonians.

F - In marine gastropods, it is not uncommon to find animals equipped with a brightly colored foot, while the shell itself is dull, like the snail photographed on this page. The evolutionary significance of this phenomenon is not always clear.

G – A Patella ferruginea grazes on the film of seaweed covering coastal rock. The extraordinary force with which its foot clings to the rock is not due, as is commonly thought, to the action of a sucker, but to the structure of its cells, which are able to anchor to any slight irregularity.

H - Anatomical structure of a common buccinum (Buccinum undatum):
1 - mouth
2 - proboscis
3 - cephalic tentacle
4 - siphon
5 - osphradium
6 - gills
7 - mantle margin
8 - heart
9 - kidney
10 - digestive glands
11 - gonads
12 - anus
13 - penis
14 - proboscis muscles

occupied by the base of the cone. But this kind of structure created some problems in terms of locomotion. The evolution of that pointed, spiral-shaped cone into a snail form, must have offered a clear advantage. The mollusk could not only retract itself into the shell (and insulate itself from the outside environment by constructing a door, the operculum, that hermetically closed the opening), but at the same time the new snail-shaped shell was easier to transport than a long cone and did not compromise the animal's mobility.

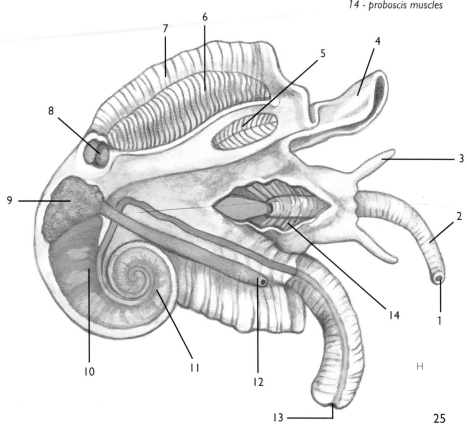

7
6
5
4
8
9
3
2
1
10
11
12
14
13

H

25

A - A prosobranch perfectly camouflaged in a colony of coelenterates. In this case, its mimicry is dual - cryptic, as the form of the animal is confused with other forms in the environment, in that its bright colours warn predators of the presence of stinging cells in the tissues.

A

It is not so simple to explain the other development in the evolution of gastropods, the dorso-ventral torsion that rotated the group of organs consisting of the mantle, shell and viscera 180 degrees away from the group formed by the head and foot. In this manner, the mantle cavity and the excretory canal of the kidneys and intestine moved to the front part of the animal, while the viscera and nerve fibers intersected to form an X. It has been hypothesized that this torsion was due to a mutation that occurred in the larval phase of a primitive gastropod, as the adult mollusk enjoyed no evolutionary advantage from the torsion. On the contrary, the little animal's excretory and reproductive organs ended up over its head, expelling their emissions into the current of water issuing from the mantle cavity very near its mouth. This obviously created serious hydraulic problems. In fossil gastropods and more primitive classes of living gastropods, the problem was resolved by opening a fissure or hole in the shell, in order to expel waste and anything else to the back, as far as possible from the mouth. In the next chapter, we will see how this torsion also resulted in profound anatomical changes.

B

C

D

F

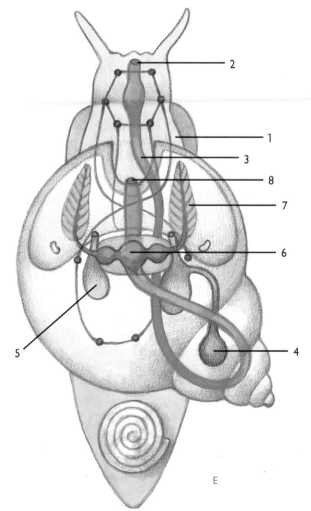

B, D and E - These illustrations reconstruct the evolutionary steps that have transformed the organization of a hypothetical primitive gastropod (B) into a present-day gastropod (E), through an intermediate phase (D) that is also hypothetical. The two decisive phenomena were the formation of the spiral shell and the 180 degree rotation of the organ group comprised of the shell, mantle and viscera, from the head-foot group.

1 - nerve fibers
2 - mouth
3 - intestine
4 - gonads
5 - kidney
6 - heart
7 - gills
8 - anus

E

G

C - A lovely photo of a triton, Charonis tritonis, taken in Hawaii. It is present in most warm and temperate seas of the world. From ancient Rome to Polynesia, its shell has been used as a war trumpet or for religious ceremonies.

F - The ornamentation of this graceful gastropod mimics the coral polyps on which it feeds.

G - The surface of the tiger cowry (Cypraea tigris) from the Indopacific is still quite common in most of its vast territory.

MOLLUSKS, ANATOMY OF A WINNER

A and B - The foot of the ancestor of the gastropods evolved differently, depending on the system of locomotion the animal adopted. In A, we can see a prosobranch with a foot similar to that of its ancestors, adapted to sliding along a substratum (reptation). In B, the foot of the opisthobranch (a Hydatina physis, photographed in Australia, where it is common as known as the rose petal bubble) allows the animal to swim at the water's surface. Opisthobranchs capable of swimming have a very light shell.

C - The drawing shows the principal elements of the common northern whelk (Buccinum undamtum), a gastropod from the Muricidae family, a subfamily of the Buccininae (which other authors consider a true family, the Buccinidae). It feeds primarily on dead animals. The relatively long siphon allows it to withdraw clean water from the environment even when it is on muddy or slimy bottoms.
1 - shell
2 - operculum
3 - inhaling siphon
4 - tentacle
5 - proboscis
6 - mouth
7 - foot
8 - mantle edge
9 - eye

These formless little creatures may be tasty when served as shellfish, but who knows how to explain their anatomy? And yet they produce shells, objects of extraordinary geometrical rigor, with a beautiful variety of forms, ornamentation and colors. It is no coincidence that some collecting books mention only shells, while the organs of their builders are dismissed as soft parts. But if you want to take a look at the fascinating chapter of natural history written by these conquerors of every corner of the sea, you should at least have some idea of how they are made and function. This takes some attention, because in the eyes of us vertebrates, mollusks look like aliens from another world. This is especially so for snails, whose anatomical structure is variable, because when they retract into their spiral-shaped shell, what happens to their bodies is a little like what happens to camping tents folded up into their bags: the parts that were on top end up on the bottom, and the things that were distant become close to each other; throughout the long period of evolution, this has caused great transformations.

But despite appearances and the extreme variety in forms of today's classes of mollusks, it has been possible to reconstruct a single original model of a mollusk. This model is only hypothetical, because, as we have seen in the preceding chapter, we will never know for certain what the progenitor of all mollusks really did, as the metamorphosis of terrestrial rocks has destroyed all fossil traces. Its organization was reconstructed based on the anatomy of present-day mollusks and what we know of those fossils. During the course of evolution, some aspects of the mollusks' original structural model were lost or radically transformed, but the legacy left by the hypothetical progenitor is still legible in all classes of the phylum.

Basic mollusk organization includes

A

B

five fundamental parts:

The foot, which is a fleshy, muscular organ used for locomotion. Its appearance may vary depending on the manner of movement. In species that move by crawling on a substratum, like most snails, the foot has essentially maintained its original appearance. It has changed greatly in species that have given up nearly all mobility, like clams, or which swim freely, like the nautilus or sea hare (Aplysia).

The head, located in front of the foot. This is the area where the mouth opens and is the site of the cerebral ganglia and sensory organs. Typically, the head of a snail has one or two

E

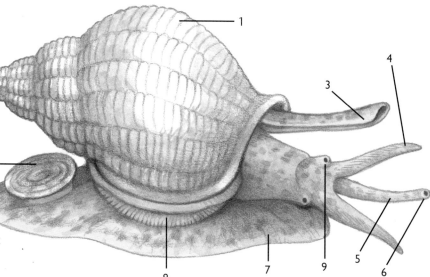

C

pairs of tentacles, one of which has eyes at the base or the summit. In more sedentary species which do not move in search of food but filter nourishment suspended in the water, the head is reduced to a mouth and little more.

The visceral sac, located on the back in relation to the foot, includes the digestive tract and the excretory, circulatory and reproductive systems (see below).

The mantle, a characteristic organ of mollusks, consists of an epidermal layer that covers the visceral sac and then descends to the base, forming a fold that surrounds the head and foot. The space that forms between the fold and the rest of the body is of particular importance, because a good part of exchanges with the outside environment occur in this cavity known as the mantle cavity or pallial cavity (from pallium, mantle in Latin). Originally a respiratory organ, it remained such for most mollusks. In almost all bivalves and in some gastropods, it also became an organ for taking in food, while in cephalopods and some bivalves, it transformed into a sort of pump that allows the animal to move according to the principle of a reaction engine.

The shell, formed by a secretion of the mantle, was originally a simple oblong, depressed cone. During the course of evolution, many species lost their shells, or transformed them into an internal structure, or kept only vestiges of them - for example in the form of cutaneous spicules in aplacophores - depending on the type of life they adopted. One of the following chapters will be devoted to the formation and different types of shells.

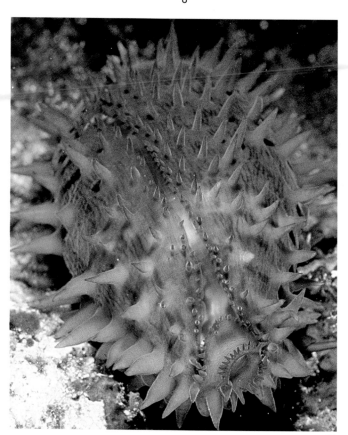

D and E - Two different ways to care for the outside of the shell. After the murex (E) builds its shell, it only repairs it in case of traumatic breaks, primarily due to attacks by predators. The husks of old shells that behave in this manner often show signs of wear, losing the periostracum and developing encrustations, with their shells furrowed by sponges and other animals. Like others in its genus, the cowry shown in photo D (a Cypraea cervus from the Caribbean province) behaves differently; throughout its life, as long as it does not feel threatened, it covers the outside of its shell with its mantle, thus keeping the surface of the shell extraordinarily shiny.

D

IN THE BELLY OF
A MARINE SNAIL

Having defined the fundamental parts of mollusk organization, let us now look at some characteristic traits of the internal anatomy of the most interesting shell builders - gastropods. Their organization is the result of complex evolution. As we have seen above, a torsion of 180 degrees in the body mass containing the mantle, visceral sac and shell, from the head-foot mass, deprived gastropods of bilateral symmetry. Consequently, the ganglia of the nervous system that ran along the two sides intersected to form a sort of X (a phenomenon known as chiastoneuria) and the organs that in an animal with a symmetrical structure normally appear in pairs,

up food. It is a ribbon-shaped membrane armed with parallel rows of teeth, acting as a flexible rasp that slides along a sort of tongue, known as an odontophore. By extroflexing the odontophore and allowing the radula to slide, the snail scrapes away food even from very hard surfaces and conveys it, well-ground, to the esophagus. The rows of teeth and the radula itself wear out rather quickly, but the snail can produce new ones continuously through specialized cells known as odontoblasts. Each species has a radula with a distinctive structure, depending on the type of food. When carefully observed under a scanning electron microscope, the

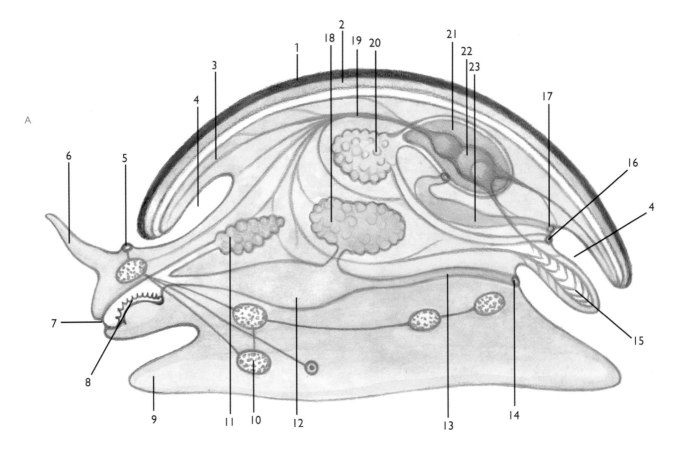

A - The drawing shows a general scheme of the internal anatomy of a mollusk.

1 - periostracum
2 - shell
3 - mantle
4 - pallial cavity
5 - eye
6 - cephalic tentacle
7 - mouth
8 - radula
9 - foot
10 - nerve ganglion
11 - salivary gland
12 - stomach
13 - intestine
14 - anus
15 - gill
16 - genital orifice
17 - excretory orifice
18 - hepatopancreas
19 - blood vessel
20 - gonads
21 - pericardium
22 - heart
23 - kidney

like kidneys, gills, atria of the heart, and the gonads, have in most gastropods become a single organ.

Digestive tract. Begins with a mouth, in which cavity are two robust plates, the jaws, and continues with the crop, which includes an organ for taking in food, the radula, that is characteristic of the phylum of mollusks. The ducts of the salivary glands open up into the crop. The digestive tube then proceeds with the stomach and back intestine. Here are some details on these organs.

Radula. Used to grasp and grind

radula gives malacologists a true identity card for classifying snails.

Salivary glands. These open into the gullet through two ducts. They produce the mucus snails need for digestion. In some families of carnivores, these transform into poison glands that can paralyze or kill prey.

Stomach. After the crop, the digestive tube continues into an esophagus, and then widens into a stomach. Food arrives here in the form of strings of particles bound together by mucus. Here it is partially digested through the activity of the crystalline style, which is located at the back of the stomach and releases enzymes for digesting glucides. Cilia on the stomach wall then carry the food to two large glands that form the spiral caecum.

Spiral caecum. This occupies a large part of the visceral sac. It both absorbs food particles and secretes enzymes. When you clean a shell by removing the soft parts, the spiral caecum looks like a dark spiral that occupies the innermost part of the shell.

Back intestine. This portion of the digestive tube runs in complex circumvolutions and ends in the anus, which opens into the mantle cavity. The current of water that runs within this organ removes catabolites from the body.

Circulatory system. The blood of mollusks is called hemolymph. Unlike the blood of vertebrates, which has numerous free cells (white corpuscles, red corpuscles, and so forth), hemolymph has only a small number of them. Oxygen is thus captured and released through two respiratory pigments dissolved within it: hemoglobin, which contains iron, and hemocyanin, which contains copper. Pumped by the heart, the hemolymph runs through circulatory vessels and gaps between the organs, to reach the tissues. The hemolymph is purified by the nephridia (kidneys) and oxygenated by the ctenidia (or gills), but often also by other vascularized tissues that play the same role in gas exchange.

Heart. This is comprised of one or two atria that receive the hemolymph oxygenated by the gills and purified by the kidneys, and pump it into the single ventricle. Using an aorta, the ventricle distributes it to various organs. In mollusks, only oxygenated hemolymph, the equivalent of our arterial blood, passes through the heart.

Excretory system. This consists of one, or sometimes two, nephridia (or kidneys) located right behind the mantle cavity. The interior of a nephridium is like a spongy sac, as its walls consist of a tissue arranged in many intricate little folds, covered with cells that contain uric acid. Here the hemolymph gives up its catabolites, urea and other nitrogenous substances, and

proceeds to the gills. The kidney expels the catabolites into the mantle cavity either through a simple orifice, or through a conduit with cilia, the ureter.

Genital apparatus. It is different for each of the three subclasses of gastropods. With a few exceptions, prosobranchs have distinct sexes, while opisthobranchs and pulmonates are almost all hermaphrodites. In less evolved prosobranchs (like limpets and topshells) there is no internal fecundation. Spermatozoa and ova from male and female gonads are released into the sea water, where fecundation takes place.

In more evolved prosobranchs (like periwinkles, cowries, and whelks) fecundation is internal, and the eggs are released into the marine environment either protected by a gelatinous mass or enclosed within egg capsules. The male has a gonad contiguous with the spiral caecum; the spermatozoa go through a prostate that runs along the bottom of the mantle cavity, parallel to the rectum. Fecundation occurs by means of a penis that may be quite large and emerges from the mollusk's head or neck, behind the right tentacle. The female genital apparatus is much more complex. From the ovary, ova

reach the albumen gland, which envelops them in a nourishing fluid, and then proceed to the capsule gland (in other species the gelatin gland), which produces the outer protection. The duct between the albumen gland and the capsule gland contains a side pocket, the spermatheca, where the male gametes are kept until used. The ovum is fertilized at the front end of the albumen gland. The female apparatus emerges just within the mantle cavity.

B and C - The drawings provide a general outline of the main internal anatomical features of a male (to the left) and female (to the right) cenogastropod prosobranch.	
1 - mouth	8 - auricle
2 - proboscis	9 - pericardium
3 - cephalic tentacle	10 - ventricle
4 - eye	11 - kidney
5 - foot	12 - operculum
6 - siphon	13 - male gonads
7 - gill	14 - anus
	15 - penis
	16 - female gonads
	17 - digestive gland
	18 - intestine
	19 - spermotheca
	20 - stomach
	21 - oviduct
	22 - female genital aperture
	23 - salivary glands

31

MOVEMENT

A

When someone is moving too slowly, we say he's going at a snail's pace. Yet, without ever quickening their pace, snails have successfully made great strides over a half a billion years. It's a sign that this is the best speed for them to meet the challenges of an aquatic environment. But just how does a snail's pace really function? In other words, how does a gastropod use its foot to crawl along a solid surface?

Experts discovered the secret of this form of locomotion, known as reptation, about 40 years ago. What

The parts of the foot alternate in the movement: the portions that do not move adhere tenaciously to the substratum, so much so that a suction cup action has been hypothesized. In reality, it is not an adhesion caused by a pneumatic depression, like a suction cup, but rather a very thorough adhesion of the foot cells, which are quite plastic and moistened with mucus, to every single irregularity of any surface they touch.

In bivalves, a class of mollusks much less mobile than gastropods, movement is by different means. For small movements on the surface of the

B, C and D - A robber waits in ambush. Using its foot, the cone Conus textile of the Indopacific, which can kill small fish by paralyzing them with its poisonous dart, lies buried in the coral sand. It stays in contact with the surrounding environment through its siphon, which can be distinguished by its alternately light and dark colored bands.

B

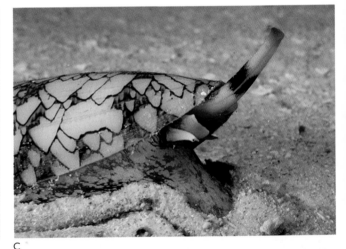

C

A - Gastropods use a highly flexible foot for movement. This muscular, well-innervated organ not only allows the mollusk to slide forward through the mechanism of reptation, but also permits it to climb up slender supports, to lift its shell from the substratum or to bury it in the sand or mud. The figure shows the trichotropid Torellia mirabilis from the Antarctic coast.

moves the mollusk forward is a wave caused by muscular contractions that moves the foot in some species forward to backward, and vice versa in other species. In the first case, common to genera like Haliotis, Trochus and Littorina, movement occurs when a small portion of the foot is raised, projected forward and once again placed on the ground; its subsequent contraction moves the part behind the foot forward. If the wave travels the other way (as has been seen in the genera Fissurella, Nerita and Turbo) the portion of the foot in contact with the substratum contracts, but the result is still the same - the gastropod moves forward.

D

E, F, H and I - The photos show a large volute, Cymbiola Imperialis, as it buries itself. Despite its massive shell, which can be as much as 25 centimeters long, the animal's large, relatively slender foot can perform the very operation quickly.

G - The drawing shows the system a bivalve, the cockle Acanthocardia Echinata, uses to enter and exit the substratum. The red foot can alternately elongate and swell, pulling the animal into the sea bed or out of it. The first drawing shows the exhaling and inhaling siphons the mollusk uses to take in oxygen-rich water and food particles and expel catabolites.

H

E

I

F

G

seabed, the foot, alternating contractions and extensions and resting on the substratum, pushes the mollusk in the desired direction. On mobile seabeds of sand and mud, the foot can bury the mollusk in the substratum with a traction movement, achieved through a series of quick swellings followed by elongations, similar to the way certain earthworms move. But some species of bivalves use their shell and mantle to move at the water's surface with remarkable speed. Thus, scallops can jump at the water's surface by snapping the two valves shut (it takes only forty-six thousandths of a second for the muscle contraction). The mollusk behaves in this manner

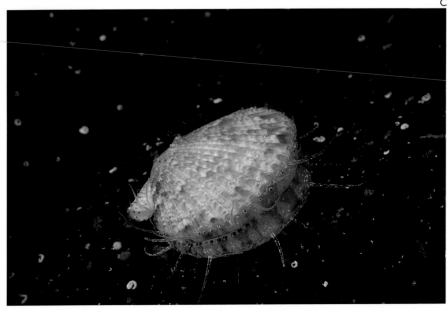

C

A

when it becomes aware of an approaching predator. If this kind of emergency situation does not exist and such rapid, lengthy movement is not necessary, the scallop expels water from its shell in various ways, achieving movement in the opposite direction from the preceding one. In both cases, movement is based on the principle of a reaction engine. In an aquarium, if we provoke a bed of scallops into feeling together, the effect is something similar to an underwater flight of butterflies.

A, C - The photos evidence two ways in wich bivalves swim. Over a long period of evolution, a few families of this class of mollusks, which had originally given up mobility and sight to live an exclusively sedentary life, feeding on detritus suspended in the water, rediscovered the advantages of movement, and at the same time developed

elementary eyes along the edges of the mantle. The picture C, a scallop from the Atlantic and Mediterranean, Aequipecten opercularis, swims on the water's surface using a jet propulsion system that is activated by opening and closing its valves. The image A, the file shell Lima hians swims by opening its valves and moving its rich crown of filaments.

B

B - The drawing shows the swimming scallop, Pecten maximus of the Atlantic. By alternately contracting and releasing its adductor muscles, the mollusk can rapidly open and close its valves, which causes a strong jet of water to spray out, resulting in an elementary but efficient form of jet propulsion.

D

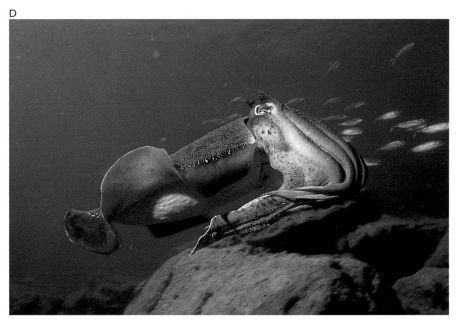

D - Of all mollusks, the cephalopods, a class of predators, have found the most brilliant solution to the problem of locomotion. Thus, the giant Australian cuttlefish, while relying on the sea bed for food, can move quite rapidly on the water's surface through the jet propulsion it achieves by expelling water through a siphon with an adjustable opening.

E - One gastropod, the Janthina, relies on currents and wind for movement. It stays afloat using a raft that it builds by forming bubbles of mucus and gluing them together. Incapable of independent movement, it is part of the plankton and feeds by preying on planktonic coelenterates that it comes upon.

The mollusks that have most highly refined the principle of reaction propulsion are the cephalopods: cuttlefish and squid are among the fastest of all marine animals.

They move using a very rapid muscular contraction (sixty-eight thousandths of a second) that expels the water in the animal's mantle through an appropriately placed siphon; by squeezing the siphon, the mollusk can regulate the speed of the water expelled and thus the speed its body moves. In this case, the principle of reaction propulsion is expressed by the formula mass of the animal multiplied by speed of the animal equals mass of the liquid multiplied by speed of the liquid, and as the two masses, the animal's and that of the liquid in its mantle sac, are fixed quantities, the speed of movement depends solely on the speed the water is expelled through the siphon.

Numerous species of gastropods and bivalves have completely given up movement as adults. In some cases they allow themselves to be carried by marine currents and become part of the plankton. This is the case of snails from the genus Janthina, who float on rafts of water bubbles held together by mucus. As we have noted, mussels anchor to the substratum with filaments of byssus. Common and thorny oysters cement a valve to the seabed. Vermetids have transformed their snail shell into a more or less worm-like tube cemented to the substratum. Date mussels (Lithophaga lithophaga) dig a tunnel in the calcareous rock and live there for their entire life, sheltered from predators, and ship-worms (Teredo navalis) use the same strategy by boring wood. Dispersion of populations in these sedentary species takes place during their larval stage.

F

G

F - Two limpets buried among the cirripeds that cover the reef. In this case, they only appear to be immobile. When it is dark, the two limpets will leave their burrows to graze on the film of algae that covers the rock. When the meal is over, they will be able to return home with no problem.

G - Among the bivalves, the scallops are known for their mobility, but Pedum spondyloidum, photographed here in the Arl atoll of the Maldives, has adopted a lifestyle different from its relatives. Its larvae settle in a hollow of a coral formation and allow the coral colony to partially surround the shell. It has just enough room to close its valves and extroflex its siphons.

E

RESPIRATION

The exchange of gases with air dissolved in the water occurs in the mantle cavity through the ctenidia, which are gills with a lamellar structure that assume various forms, depending on the species. The water is circulated in the mantle cavity by cilia that create a current through their movement. In many species, the need to bury themselves in the sand or mud has led to the transformation of a flap of the mantle into an inhaling siphon, a proboscis-shaped appendage that inhales the oxygen-rich water

A, B - Respiratory structure of a gastropod (A) and a bivalve (B). A – the water rich in dissolved oxygen is sucked in by the siphon through the gills (1) and is subsequently returned to the environment through the shell cavity. B - In bivalves the water, after having been aspired through the siphon (2) and having passed through the bronchi, is expelled through the siphon (3).

from the substratum. In other species there is also an exhaling siphon that has the task of removing oxygen-poor water and catabolites from the mantle cavity.

Depending on the position of the gills from the heart, marine gastropods can be divided into two large subclasses: the prosobranchs, with gills in front of the heart, and opisthobranchs, who have them turned toward the caudal area. In opisthobranchs, the nerve ganglia do not intersect, perhaps because the original torsion of the body was followed by a straightening. The third subclass of gastropods, the pulmonates (of which only very few species are marine) have transformed the mantle cavity into a sort of lung that can take in oxygen directly from the atmosphere. There are also a few cases of mollusks that have both gills and lungs and can breathe either in or out of the water.

1 - gills
2 - inhaling siphon
3 - exhaling siphon
4 - hypobranchial gland
5 - osphradium
6 - pallial cavity

C – The movements of this gastropod on a uneven surface are controlled by the statolite, a minute lime formation that stimulates the nerve endings of the foot.

D – A strombus explores the environment with its eyes and antennae, whose chemical sensors supply the nervous system with vital information about the environment.

THE NERVOUS SYSTEM AND SENSORY ORGANS

Depending on the type of life they lead and the relationships they establish with their environment, mollusks have developed very diverse nervous systems. The more sedentary species, like the bivalves that feed by filtering particles suspended in the water, in general have elementary nervous systems, with nerve cells scattered along a few cords, connected to each other by simple ganglia that perform local functions. At the other extreme, we find more dynamic organisms, like carnivorous hunters who must identify, follow and capture prey. It is no coincidence that these species have highly complex nervous structures and sensory organs, with ganglia that resemble the brain of vertebrates.

Sensory organs are also closely related to the animal's relationship with the environment. With regard to

C

sight, the gamut runs from organisms with just a few photosensitive cells, capable of informing the animal of whether there is light and shadow in its environment and nothing more, all the way to species that have developed eyes with crystalline that can focus on distant objects. The most evolved mollusk, the octopus, is capable of distinguishing various geometric forms. Aquarium experiments have shown that the octopus is capable of memorizing these geometric forms by associating them with pleasant or unpleasant sensations created by the experimenter.

In the great majority of mollusks, however, sight is not primary among their sensory endowments, all the more so because much of the phylum prefers poorly illuminated or completely dark environments. Many species pass the daylight hours buried under the sand or mud of the seabed

and come out only at night. How do they orient themselves, and how, for example, do they find living prey or the carcass of the fish to devour? It is clear that marine mollusks have a complete battery of chemical sensors that permits them to sniff out currents of water and take advantage of the information they receive. It is much more complex to identify in the laboratory which sensitive cells are used for which tasks in the chemical exploration of the environment.

Researchers are particularly interested in the osphradium, a plume-shaped organ traversed by a nerve, that many gastropods have at the base of the gills. Located in an excellent position for analyzing the flow of water inhaled by the mollusk, the osphradium in effect seems to be a switchboard for detecting chemical substances, although it probably combines this function with testing the physical consistency of the solid particles suspended in the water, to protect the gills from the risk of clogging.

With most of the body enclosed in the shell, many species of mollusks use various appendages for tactile functions. Sometimes these are hairs or slender filaments, which in many cases seem to be sensitive to both chemical and tactile stimulation. The edge of the mantle is the part of the body best equipped for this purpose, at least for most

D

species. All species are also equipped with small organs that transmit information to the nervous system on the animal's position within its environment. At the base of the foot's nerve ganglia there are two pockets, the statocysts, within which moves a tiny calcareous formation, and the statolith, which by stimulating the nerve endings orients the animal and gives it equilibrium.

E - The drawing shows the structure of a snail's nervous system. The process of cephalization (1), i.e. thickening of the ganglia in the head to form a brain, is still quite modest. Note the digestive tract the x-shaped intersection of the nerve cords due to the torsion the snail underwent during the course of evolution. Neurons connect the cephalic ganglia to the eyes (2), the tactile and chemical sensors of the tentacles (3), the heart (4), the digestive tract (5), the gills (6) and the other organs.

E

A

A, F - To a casual observer, marine gastropods seem to have no sight organs. But by focusing in closer, the underwater photographer was able to see the eyes of these two strombids from the Pacific, Strombus dentatus (A) and Lambis (F).

1

2

3

B

4

E

C

D

B, E and G - Mollusks who live in the dark or feed as parasites or detritovores have no sense of sight. Sight is quite poor in bivalves like the scallops, whose eyes are only capable of perceiving variations in the intensity of environmental light. In relatively primitive snails like the trochids, the eye (B), consisting of the vitreous chamber (1), retina (2) and optical nerve (3), is quite primitive and perceives only vague images. In more evolved mollusk predators like the murices, the eye (E) has a crystalline lens (4), and the images are more distinct. In *highly evolved cephalopods like squid, the eye (G) also has an iris (5) and optical ganglion (6). The images come into focus in essentially the same way as in vertebrates, not by modifying the form of the crystalline lens, but by moving the lens back and forth from the retina.*

F

H, I and J - The strip tease of a beautiful Cypraea pantherina from the Indopacific. When it is not disturbed, the cowry (H) grazes peacefully on the algae from the sea bed, with its shell wrapped in its semitransparent mantle. As soon as it detects the presence of potential danger, it begins to retract its mantle, formed of very delicate tissue (I), which it then hides safely under its robust shell (J).

H

C, D - The evolutionary reconquest of the sense of sight has led to the development of a series of ocelli on the edge of the mantle of bivalves. These eyes have a very limited capacity, and act primarily in detecting the intensity of light in the environment, but are nonetheless sufficient to allow the animal to perceive the presence of danger and close its valves. This scallop from the Pacific Northwest coast (Chlamys hericia) (C), camouflages itself using a purple sponge encrusted on the upper valve, while a burying bivalve from the Red Sea (D) peeps out of the coral in which it has settled, showing off a spectacular series of red eyes.

I

G

6

5

J

FEEDING

During the course of their long evolution, mollusks have experimented with various feeding systems: there are herbivore, carnivore and detritovore species (who collect the particles of organic detritus that are continuously deposited on seabeds), suspension feeders (who capture organic particles that float at the water's surface) and parasites, who feed from the tissues of other animals by settling within them (endoparasites) or on them (ectoparasites). Among the carnivores, there are lazy species, who feed on dead animals (necrophagia) or animals attached to the substratum. This is the case of murices, who graze on oysters, acorn barnacles and mussels. There are also, however, active carnivores (for example, cephalopods like the cuttlefish and octopus), who can hunt moving prey due to their speed, or carnivores that use ingenious methods

A - This is an example of a radula that is not highly specialized, used by less evolved snails like the cowries. The ribbon (1) is activated by a muscle (2) located behind the mouth. It has a great many rows of teeth armed with cusps (3) that can grind plant tissue. In the back portion (4), the rows of teeth are gradually produced by a special organ as the rows at the front wear out.

C, D, I and J - In this exceptional sequence, a Conus purpurascens of western Mexico shoots a dart into a small fish that has ventured near it, paralyzes it with a lightning injection of poison, and finally begins to swallow it. Cones like the one shown in the photo, can be life-threatening to man.

E - This image shows the dart protruding from the proboscis of a Conus striatus from the Indopacific. A chemical analysis shows that cones inject their victims with a whole cocktail of toxic substances. The first ones to take effect create a tetanic contraction in the victim, to prevent any coordinated reaction; then substances that cause the vital systems to collapse and the organism to relax go into effect, allowing it to be ingested by the mollusk.

F, G and H - These cross-sections show how a radula in a snail like a cowry functions. Within the mouth (1), the ribbon of teeth (2) that makes up the radula slides back and forth, using a mechanical action just like a carpenter's rasp. It carries food particles (7) to the esophagus (6). The radula moves through the action of a muscle (4) anchored to a cartilage (5). The "radula pocket" (8) produces new teeth to replace those that wear out. In very primitive gastropods like the trochids, the radula consists of rows (3) containing dozens of teeth, which decrease in number in more evolved families.

B - The drawing shows how the radula works in an evolved snail like the cone. The chitinous ribbon in herbivorous or perforating mollusks has become just one tooth (1) transformed into a poison-filled harpoon - essentially a syringe. Harpoons are produced (2) and continuously replaced, like the teeth of different type of radulae. One by one, they descend into the proboscis (4), where they are filled with poison from a salivary gland (3) transformed into a poison gland.

of lying in ambush, like the cones, which are snails capable of striking their prey with a proboscis armed with a dart that injects a paralyzing poison. Each species of cone specializes in hunting other mollusks, worms or even fish, but only the fish eaters have a poison powerful enough to pose a mortal threat to humans as well. Cones are the only family of mollusks whose close observation and collection require much experience and a great deal of caution.

We have seen that to capture and grind up food, mollusks have developed an organ unique in the animal world, the radula. Bivalves do not have a radula, but have developed ingenious systems to capture food particles from the water they inhale as they breathe through the gills, killing two birds with one stone, so

A

B

D - The drawing shows a predator snail, a moon, attacking a bivalve. Its crucial weapon is its radula, which allows the attacker to drill the shell and suck out the tissues with its proboscis, after which it abandons the empty shell.

E - The radula is a fundamental invention in snails, and has been modified differently according to species. This chitinous rasp, which is always being replaced, can scrape away food particles from vegetation, bore through the shell of prey, or even, using a tooth transformed into a harpoon, paralyze prey by injecting a cocktail of refined poisons. In A, through the enlarged opening of the mouth (1) of a predator snail (like the sand moon), we can see a portion of the radula, consisting of three rows of three teeth each (2), plus an auxiliary structure (3). By sliding the radula within the oral cavity and rotating the proboscis, the snail digs a perfectly circular furrow into the shell of the Cardium (4) that becomes a hole when the operation is completed (5). The predator then inserts its proboscis into its prey's shell and sucks out its tissues.

A, B and C - In this image captured in the Rangiroa Lagoon in Polynesia, the triton (Charonia tritonis) attacks a crown-of thorns starfish (Acanthaster planci). Blocked by the triton's muscular foot (A, B), the starfish reacts and succeeds in making a counterattack against the aggressor, who then sprays it with a white, poisonous substance (C). The starfish dies. The triton takes six hours to devour it. Acanthaster planci feeds on coral polyps and is a danger to the integrity of the reef; the triton is thus a protected species in many countries precisely because it prevents this starfish's uncontrolled proliferation.

C

to speak. The vibrating motion of a system of cilia forces water from the outside to the gills, located in the mantle cavity. For bivalves who live embedded in the substratum, the water flows through an inhaling siphon that may be even longer than the rest of the body. The gills are very developed and have complex forms. While their well-vascularized tissue captures oxygen dissolved in the water, special cilia systems, often equipped with mucus, dispose of inedible particles and convey useful particles to the mouth. The water utilized is expelled from the mantle cavity at the back end of the animal (through an exhaling siphon, for bivalves who live buried) along with catabolites, faeces and renal excretions.

E

D

F and G - The picture shows a case of cannibalism among mollusks: a large moon snail from the Atlantic coast of North America, the Lunatia heros *(which can exceed 12 centimeters in diameter), attacks a fellow member of its species by holding it down with its foot and perforating the shell with its radula. When the hole is complete, the attacking snail inserts its proboscis into the flesh of its victim and devours its tissues. Usually, however,* Lunatia heros *hunts by moving under the sand of the sea bed and attacking the bivalves that lie buried there.*

F

G

43

A - A Colubraria
explores a shark's
scar in an attempt to
reach the fish's
internal tissues and
suck its blood.

A

B

C

B - Three tiny
wentletraps from the
species Epitonium
billeeanum *feed on
the tissues of coral
polyps from the genus
Tubastrea, at
Richelieu Rock in the
Andamane Sea
(Thailand).*

C - A predator turning
into prey: in the sea of
the Galapagos Islands
in the East Pacific, a
large fasciolariid,
Pleuroploca
princeps, *successfully
attacks a murex, an
active predator of
bivalves.*

D - *Three specimens of the turbinid* Tegula *graze on the tissues of a large sea-tangle along the coast of California.*

D

E

E - *An example of parasitic and vampire-type behavior: the gastropod at the center of the photo, a* Colubraria obscura *from the* Fasciolariidae *family, has climbed onto the bubble of mucus that the parrotfish* Scarus soridus, *from the coral reefs of Thailand, has used to wrap around itself for protection. The mollusk has penetrated the mucus with its long, thin proboscis, which it inserts into the mouth of the sleeping fish to suck blood from its tissues.*

45

REPRODUCTION

The reproductive strategies of mollusks vary from species to species. Less developed representatives of the phylum use external fecundation: males and females discharge gametes into the water contemporaneously, and the chance encounter of an ovum with a spermatozoon creates the larva of a new individual. Clearly, this is an enormously expensive strategy in terms of energy, because only a tiny fraction of the gametes hits the mark. Obviously, it is practiced only by aquatic mollusks.

More evolved species use internal fecundation, which occurs when individuals of different sexes or hermaphrodites mate. Internal fecundation permits high rates of reproduction using a relatively small number of gametes. It also permits the female reproductive system to protect the eggs from the outside environment by giving them a shell. In numerous species, the eggs are further protected by wrapping them in egg capsules. On the

A

B

C

D

E

F

A - A limpet from the Antarctic province, Nacella concinna, from the South Orkney Islands, is releasing zygotes into the open water.

B - A Tridacna gigas, the largest bivalve in the world, emits a little cloud of ova into the water. Fecundation will take place in the open water, when ova encounter spermatozoa from the same species. The success of this external reproduction is based on the immense number of zygotes released into the sea: hundreds of millions from each individual reproducer.

C, E, F - During the course of evolution, mollusks have been through many reproductive strategies. Within the phylum, there are forms of external reproduction, with ova and spermatozoa released into the sea, and internal fecundation of the ova, where individuals of the opposite sex or hermaphrodites mate directly or at a distance. There are also forms of panthenogenesis (fecundation without the male). Here, we see 3 systems mollusks use to bring the sperm to the ovum.

C - A trochid spermatozoon (1) moves by itself, using a flagellum (4).

E - the spermatozoa (1) travel in packs (spermatozeugmae) within particular cells specialized in movement: the one illustrated is a spermatozeugma from Ceritiopsidae.

F - In cephalopods like the squid, the mass of spermatozoa (1) travels protected by a tunic (2) within a complex organ, the spermatophore. This tunic has an ejaculating organ (3) and a flagellum (4) for propulsion in open water.

G

H

other hand, growth of the egg within the female system and the production of already formed individuals (viviparism) is quite rare among mollusks.

We have seen that hermaphroditism is the rule among opisthobranchs and pulmonates. The anatomical details of the reproductive organs normally prevent self-fecundation, and this eliminates any possible genetic impoverishment of the species. In other words, for fecundation to occur, two hermaphroditic individuals must meet, and the male organ of each one must fecundate the female organ of the other. What could be the evolutionary advantage to this reproductive strategy? The hypothesis advanced is this: snails move quite slowly, and encounters among individuals are relatively rare. If the sexes were separate, the probability that these encounters would occur between males and females would be no more than 50%. With both sexes in the same individual, however, probabilities of encounters at least theoretically useful for reproduction rise to 100%.

I - An unfertilized ovum of a mollusk. We can see the nucleus (1) with the chromosomes (2).

J - The embryos can be seen forming through the transparent egg capsules of Nucella lapillus.

K - This image shows hatching Littorina eggs. Most of the species of this genus of gastropods, which live in the supralittoral or tidal zone, do not form larva capable of swimming in the open water, but directly develop little snails that crawl away on the substratum after birth.

D - Two Cypraea talpa deposits eggs in the waters of Isla del Cocos in Costa Rica.

G - Egg capsules deposited by two Conus scalaris, a species from the more primitive family of conids, in western Mexico.

H - Egg being deposited by the Bulla gouldiana of California, the largest bullid in existence (its shell is up to 6.4 centimeters long). As is usual for

opisthobranchs, individuals of this species are hermaphrodites. The eggs are released in long, thin, gelatinous strings that form tangled masses.

J

I

2

1

K

47

A

F

B

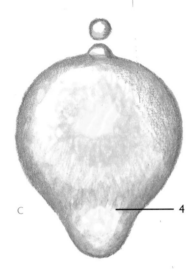

C

1

2

3

4

B, C, G, H, I, J, M, N development stage.
B - The spermatozoon (3) enters the ovum and reaches the nucleus (2) (the polar bodies of the ovum are indicated under 1).
C - The union of the gametes, forms the first cell of the new individual, the zygote (the egg sac in 4).
G - Two cell development stage.
H - Four cell

development stage.
J - Multi-cell development stage.
K - Embryo (trochophore) at 22 hours of development (5 apical cilia).
M - Trochophore at 30 hours.
N - Trochophore at 44 hours, enlarged approximately 300 times:
6 apical tuft;
7 velum;
8 larval mouth.

D

G

E

A - Three egg capsules of Nassarius reticulatus. This common snail of European seas deposits about a hundred of these capsules at a time.

D - Strange necklaces are not uncommon on sandy or muddy sea beds: these are the eggs of the moon snail, which we see in this photo as it deposits its eggs.

H

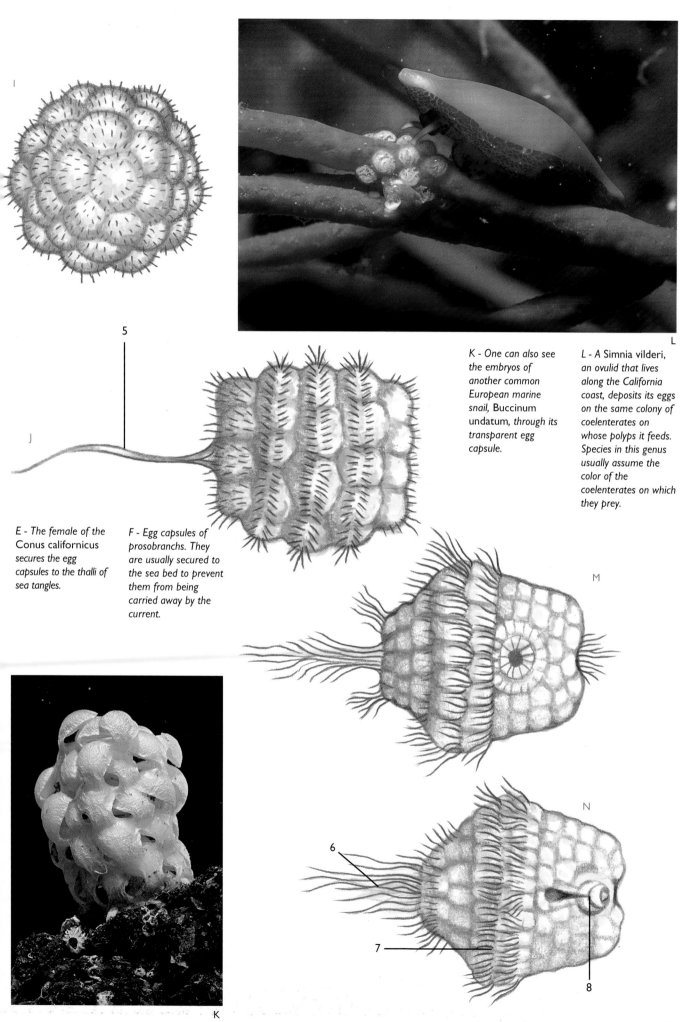

I

5

J

K - One can also see the embryos of another common European marine snail, Buccinum undatum, *through its transparent egg capsule.*

L - A Simnia vilderi, an ovulid that lives along the California coast, deposits its eggs on the same colony of coelenterates on whose polyps it feeds. Species in this genus usually assume the color of the coelenterates on which they prey.

L

E - The female of the Conus californicus secures the egg capsules to the thalli of sea tangles.

F - Egg capsules of prosobranchs. They are usually secured to the sea bed to prevent them from being carried away by the current.

M

N

6

7

8

K

49

A

D

5

4

3

1

2

B

E

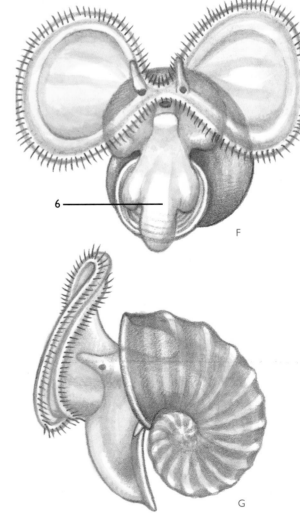

6

F

G

A, B - The development of veliger larva in a bivalve.
A - The structure of a 5-day old embryo.
B - The veliger at 15 days old. One can distinguish the gills (1), the foot (2), the embryonic shell (3), the adductor muscle (4) and the stomach (5).

C, H - Two veligers of littoral mollusks from Australia's Great Barrier Reef. The shell, already at the embryonic stage, and part of the digestive tract, are visible in both. In C, the operculum has also already formed. The length of larval life varies greatly from species to species. When it is prolonged for entire months, as for the triton, it encourages the dispersion of the species over vast areas.

D, K - Pictured are two pelagic mollusks, an Atlanta (D) and a Carinaria cristata (K), prosobranch gastropods that are part of the plankton even as adults. Most mollusks in this subclass flow with the plankton only during their larval existence.

C

H

E, F, G, I, J - Some phases in veliger larval development of gastropods. This is a more evolved larval form than the trochophore, and is characteristic of the phylum of mollusks. In families that have veliger-type embryos, the trochophore form is only a stage of development within the egg. The velum, which allows the veliger to move freely through the water (although the movement is limited, within the plankton carried by sea currents), may take different forms: two lobes as in E and F, four lobes as in I (larva of Philberta gracilis) or six lobes as in J (larva of Aporrhais pespelecani). In this phase of their development, gastropods have a distinct head, equipped with eyes and tentacles, a larval shell and an early development of the foot (F-6).

I

J

K

L

In marine mollusks, when the egg hatches, a larva generally appears that will float with the currents as part of the plankton. The larva may have a trochophore form (that is, a simple ciliated top, similar to the larva of other phyla of invertebrates) or a veliger form, which is a more evolved larva, characteristic of mollusks. The individual is already able to form a little shell, generally different in appearance from the adult shell, and has wing-shaped growths (the velum), equipped with cilia it uses to move through the water and obtain food. At the end of the larval period, the mollusk allows itself to fall to the seabed: if it finds the right

L - A group of immature Conus anemone, a very common cone along the southwestern coasts of Australia. Often, a number of females in this species will gather in groups to lay their eggs in the same area.

51

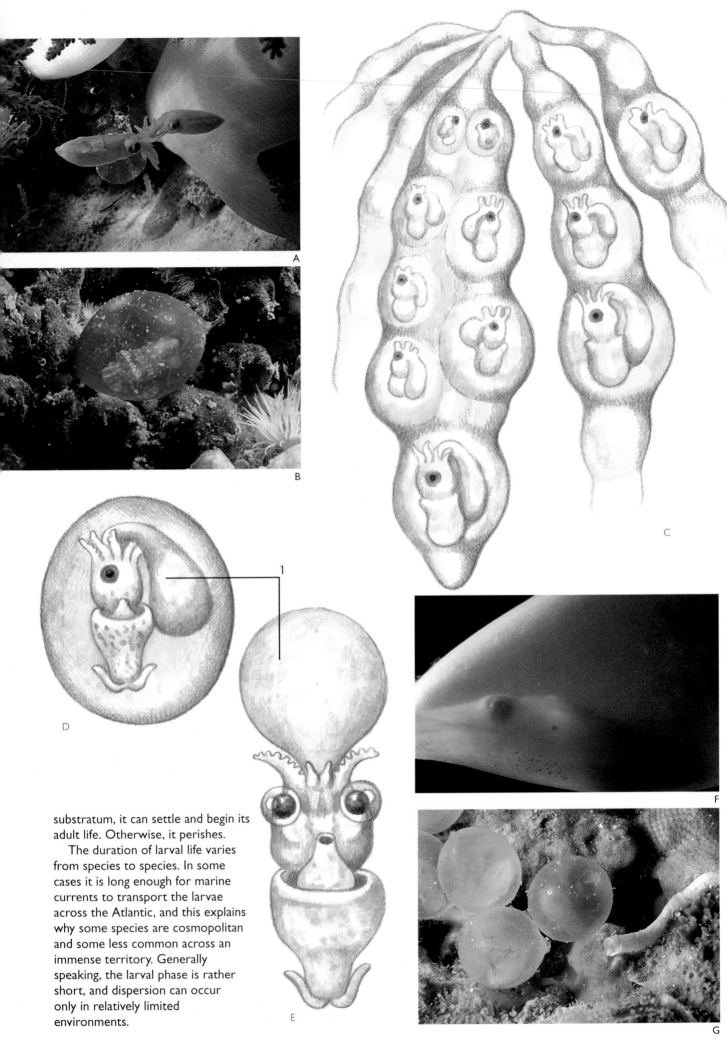

substratum, it can settle and begin its adult life. Otherwise, it perishes.

The duration of larval life varies from species to species. In some cases it is long enough for marine currents to transport the larvae across the Atlantic, and this explains why some species are cosmopolitan and some less common across an immense territory. Generally speaking, the larval phase is rather short, and dispersion can occur only in relatively limited environments.

A

B

C

D

1

E

F

G

A – Cuttlefish mating. The cephalopods have developed a variety of very effective systems to avoid the loss of spermatozoa in the marine environment. Mating sometimes takes place at close quarters, whilst on other occasions organs released from the male's body swim towards the female.

B - The formation of a mollusk larva seen through the translucent membrane of the egg.

H

I

C, D, E, I - The stages of development of a squid. In the cluster of egg capsules, about ten centimeters high (C), each embryo develops by assuming the basic structure of the adult individual (D) and gradually absorbing the yolk in the sac (1). When it hatches from the egg, the little squid continues to empty the yolk sac (E) until it completely disappears. At this stage (I), the squid begins its life as a pelagic hunter. Its first food will be tiny forms of planktonic life.

J

L

K

F - A giant of the sea takes shape: the embryo of an Australian giant cuttlefish (Sepia apama) inside its egg.

G - Cuttlefish eggs photographed on a detrital sea bed in Yemen.

H - The female argonaut has always elicited the interest of natural history experts because it builds a unique, elegant pseudo-shell that it carries with it in the high sea just to hold its eggs. The picture shows the birth of argonauts before the walls of the mother's pseudo-shell.

J, K, L - A mass of Argonauta nodosa eggs almost ready to hatch. In the image (L) a newborn argonaut faces a perilous period of life in the plankton.

53

B - The drawing shows a succession of layers that form the shell, seen here in cross-section. 1 - periostracum, made of protein substances; 2 and 3 - the ostracum, formed of crystals of calcite (2) or aragonite with intersecting plates (3); 4 - hypostracum, formed of plates of mother-of-pearl running parallel along the shell's surface.

A - The illustration outlines the process of shell formation in a bivalve. The outer pallial epithelium (1) produces the periostracum (3) in the periostracal fold (2). The cells of the inner pallial epithelium (5) produce (4) the kaleite prisms of the ostracum (6), while the innermost area (7) produces crystals of aragonite that are used to build the hypostracum (8). The mantle (9) has a retractor muscle (10) that can pull it back into the shell.

Marine mollusks build their shells with the calcium carbonate they find in food and sea water. Specialized cells found at the edge of the mantle crystallize calcium carbonate into two fundamental forms: calcite, with prism-shaped crystals, or aragonite, with lamellar crystals. The shell is built by imprisoning the crystals within the weave of a network of organic material, the conchiolin, which, chemically speaking, is a polysaccharide similar to the chitin that forms the exoskeleton of insects. A small quantity of water is also imprisoned within the shell's structure. This explains why a shell, which may at first sight seem only a piece of limestone, is actually a "living rock", which may deteriorate with time and through the effect of light rays.

A shell has three layers: outside there is the periostracum, which is a

covering of conchiolin only, and is often brown or blackish in color. It is absent in some families, like cowries, and often appears eroded even when the mollusk is living, and dissolves quite rapidly after the shell is empty and exposed to the elements. Souvenir shell vendors always eliminate it to improve the shell's appearance, while specialized sellers and demanding collectors are careful not to destroy it. In fact, every collection should have at least one specimen that is as close as possible to how nature made it.

The next layer is the ostracum:

E

formed of calcite crystals, it is the hard and permanent part of the shell. Within this is the hypostracum, which is rather thin, formed of lamellar, unbroken aragonite. In some families, these hexagonal lamellae, cemented together in overlapping layers like the rows of bricks in walls, take the form of mother-of-pearl, a substance that is not only beautifully iridescent, but is also hard - two times harder than industrially-produced synthetic ceramic.

The part of the mollusk that builds

C - The extraordinary iridescence of the mother-of-pearl of the paua, an abalone from New Zealand (Haliotis iris). This is the innermost layer of the shell, formed by sheets of crystallized calcium in the form of aragonite.

D - A precious black pearl from Tahiti, produced by a Polynesian subspecies of the pearl oyster, Pinctada margaritifera cumingi. Having become impossible to find in the natural state (in 1970, not one pearl was found in the 300,000 oysters collected in the Takapoto lagoon), it is now produced in cultivated pearl beds.

E, F - In nature, the instructions for building a logarithmic spiral shell are written in the mollusk's genes. But we can ask a computer to emulate nature by providing it an appropriate mathematical function.

The polygon outline of the electronically invented shell structure (E). The computer coverage of the polygons creates a shell that is extraordinarily similar to what can be found on a beach (F).

the shell is the edge of the mantle We have seen that the mantle cavity is an extremely important organ for the animal's relationships with the outside environment.

We can thus see how the evolution of the shell may reflect the transformation of the mantle and its cavity. For example, when a gastropod equips itself with siphons to pump water in or out of the mantle cavity, its shell acquires siphonal canals. This is a very important aspect in identifying the systematic position of a shell and the family to which it belongs.

F

A, C -When X-rayed, shells with an elongated spire like the Fasciolaria lignaria pictured in A, often exhibit the type of coiling shown in the radiograph (C). Here, the coil axis, the columella, is sinuous.

A

C

B

B, D - The X-ray picture reveals the extraordinary elegance of the internal structure of the globular shell of Tonna galea, *a large ton from the European seas.*

E

F

D

E - The shells, observed by X-ray, reveal a perfect geometry that externed observation could only imagine. Despite the variety of aesthetic solutions, the shell uses only a few fundamental geometric figures, primarily the logarithmic spiral, the cone and the circle.

F - Three examples of the pelagic snail Janthina janthina. *The shell of this species, which lives floating in the plankton, is extremely thin and light.*

A, C and D - A side (C), front (D), and cross-section (A) view of a nautilus shell of Nautilus pompilius. This cephalopod, which lives in the Southwest Pacific, has four gills (other cephalopods have only two) and has a symmetrical flat shell. The shell is also convoluted, as the last whorl covers all the other whorls. The cross-section reveals another peculiarity of the nautilus shell that makes it different from all other gastropods; it is divided into chambers, which the nautilus gradually abandons as it grows. Divided by septa, the chambers connect through a series of small holes that run through the entire spiral. The mollusk, which can take in or expel gas from the chambers, also uses its shell for vertical movements in the water, as a fish does with its air bladder, changing its specific weight.

B

A

C

D

B, E – A side view (B) and a front view (E) of the nautilus shell, photographed using X-rays: the internal structure shows how the shell is formed, through the construction of cells abandoned by the mollusc as it grows. The result possesses a geometrical purity, an essential elegance and a fluidity of form which even an artist would find difficult to match.

E

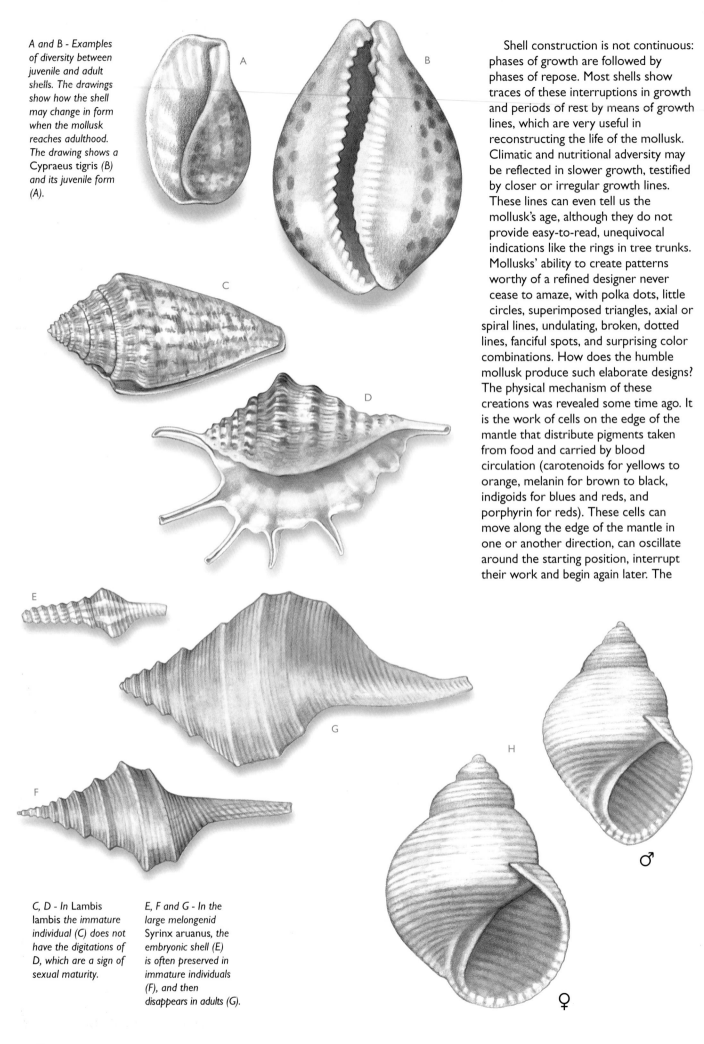

A and B - Examples of diversity between juvenile and adult shells. The drawings show how the shell may change in form when the mollusk reaches adulthood. The drawing shows a Cypraeus tigris (B) and its juvenile form (A).

Shell construction is not continuous: phases of growth are followed by phases of repose. Most shells show traces of these interruptions in growth and periods of rest by means of growth lines, which are very useful in reconstructing the life of the mollusk. Climatic and nutritional adversity may be reflected in slower growth, testified by closer or irregular growth lines. These lines can even tell us the mollusk's age, although they do not provide easy-to-read, unequivocal indications like the rings in tree trunks. Mollusks' ability to create patterns worthy of a refined designer never cease to amaze, with polka dots, little circles, superimposed triangles, axial or spiral lines, undulating, broken, dotted lines, fanciful spots, and surprising color combinations. How does the humble mollusk produce such elaborate designs? The physical mechanism of these creations was revealed some time ago. It is the work of cells on the edge of the mantle that distribute pigments taken from food and carried by blood circulation (carotenoids for yellows to orange, melanin for brown to black, indigoids for blues and reds, and porphyrin for reds). These cells can move along the edge of the mantle in one or another direction, can oscillate around the starting position, interrupt their work and begin again later. The

C, D - In Lambis lambis the immature individual (C) does not have the digitations of D, which are a sign of sexual maturity.

E, F and G - In the large melongenid Syrinx aruanus, the embryonic shell (E) is often preserved in immature individuals (F), and then disappears in adults (G).

1

I

2

J, K - In these illustrations, we see the formation of sculptures and designs on the surface of a shell (K). To make the protuberance (4), the mantle edge first forms a small fold (1), which is then accentuated in (2) and (3). The protuberance is complete when the mantle gradually reduces the fold, finally becoming flat again. The colorful designs are formed through two distinct phenomena. In the first, pigment cells migrate along the edge of the mantle. When they distance themselves at regular intervals, a semicircle

K

H, I - Besides age, other factors make two seemingly different shells members of the same species. In H (Littorina pintado), we see an example of sexual dimorphism. The female has a larger and more bulging shell, to allow for the internal development of the eggs. In I, the Nucella lapillus of calm waters (1) has less and brighter colours than the more robust shell and with more pronounced ribs than a conspecific (2) exposed to the movement of the waves (2).

movements, which are at right angles from the direction of advancement and pauses in constructing the shell, explain how designs and colors are created. The shade of colors can change with the growth of the mollusk or a dietary or environmental change, for example a variation in marine salinity, a rather frequent occurrence in closed bodies of water into which large rivers flow. It is not easy to understand what advantage the mollusk gains from all this artistic ability. Its designs do not always seem to have a mimetic or dissuasive function, even more so because they are often hidden by the periostracum.

J

3

4

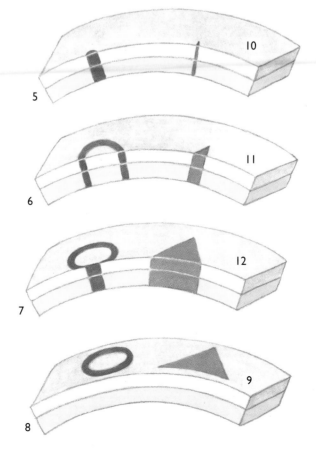

5

6

7

8

9

10

11

12

is formed (phases 5 and 6), and when they draw closer together again (phase 7), the circle closes (8) and the cells cease their activity. Intermittent pigment cells (the second type of phenomenon) create a triangle (9). The cells begin activity in (10), activate other symmetrical cells (11) and (12), and then cease activity. The phenomena of migration and intermittence, often combined, explain the fantastic creative ability of mollusks.

A

spire

Height

Last whorl

Front end (or base)

D

E

5

C

2   3

B

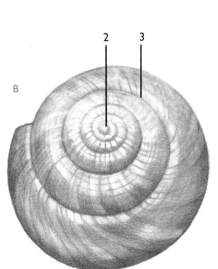

A, B and C -
Nomenclature for a
shell and its
ornamentation:

1 - Apex
2 - Protoshell
3 - Suture
4 - Indentation (or whorl)
5 - Umbilicus
6 - Shoulder
7 - Axial striae
8 - Reticular sculpture
9 - Mammillary
    sculpture
10 - Spiral striae

11 - Spines
12 - Columellar fold
13 - Columella
14 - Spiral ribs
15 - Axial ribs
16 - Tubercle
17 - Varix
18 - Outer lip
19 - Digitation
20 - Labial folds
21 - Aperture
22 - Inner lip
23 - Siphonal canal
24 - Back cavity
25 - Front cavity
26 - Teeth

62

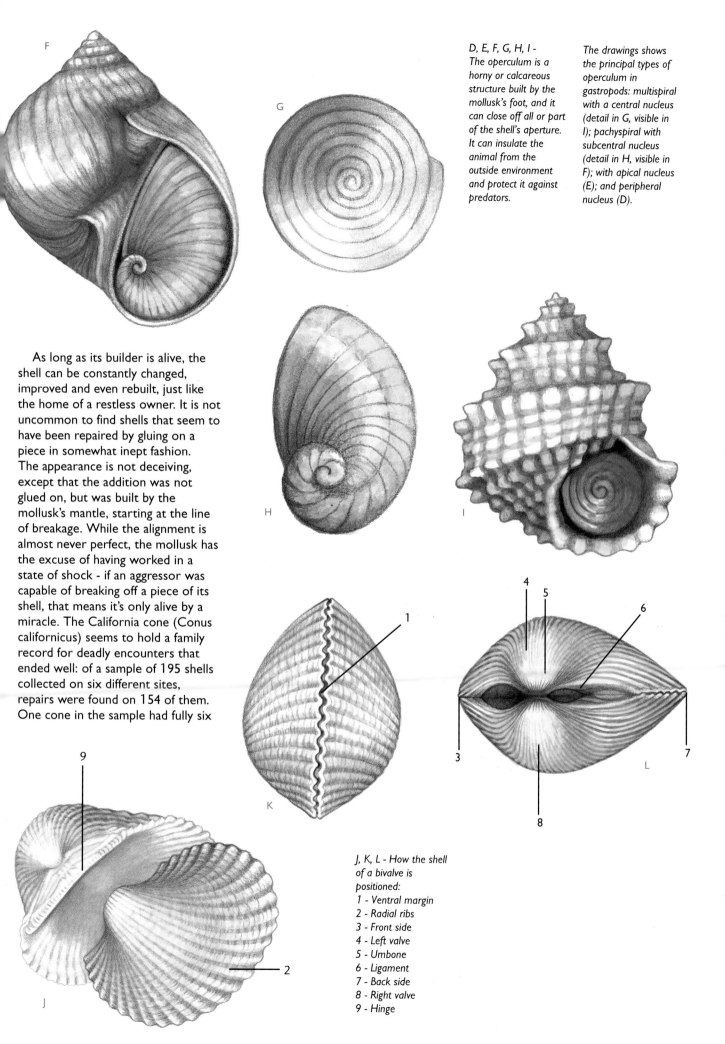

F

G

D, E, F, G, H, I - The operculum is a horny or calcareous structure built by the mollusk's foot, and it can close off all or part of the shell's aperture. It can insulate the animal from the outside environment and protect it against predators.

The drawings shows the principal types of operculum in gastropods: multispiral with a central nucleus (detail in G, visible in I); pachyspiral with subcentral nucleus (detail in H, visible in F); with apical nucleus (E); and peripheral nucleus (D).

As long as its builder is alive, the shell can be constantly changed, improved and even rebuilt, just like the home of a restless owner. It is not uncommon to find shells that seem to have been repaired by gluing on a piece in somewhat inept fashion. The appearance is not deceiving, except that the addition was not glued on, but was built by the mollusk's mantle, starting at the line of breakage. While the alignment is almost never perfect, the mollusk has the excuse of having worked in a state of shock - if an aggressor was capable of breaking off a piece of its shell, that means it's only alive by a miracle. The California cone (Conus californicus) seems to hold a family record for deadly encounters that ended well: of a sample of 195 shells collected on six different sites, repairs were found on 154 of them. One cone in the sample had fully six

H

I

1

9

4

5

6

3

7

8

L

K

J

2

J, K, L - How the shell of a bivalve is positioned:
1 - Ventral margin
2 - Radial ribs
3 - Front side
4 - Left valve
5 - Umbone
6 - Ligament
7 - Back side
8 - Right valve
9 - Hinge

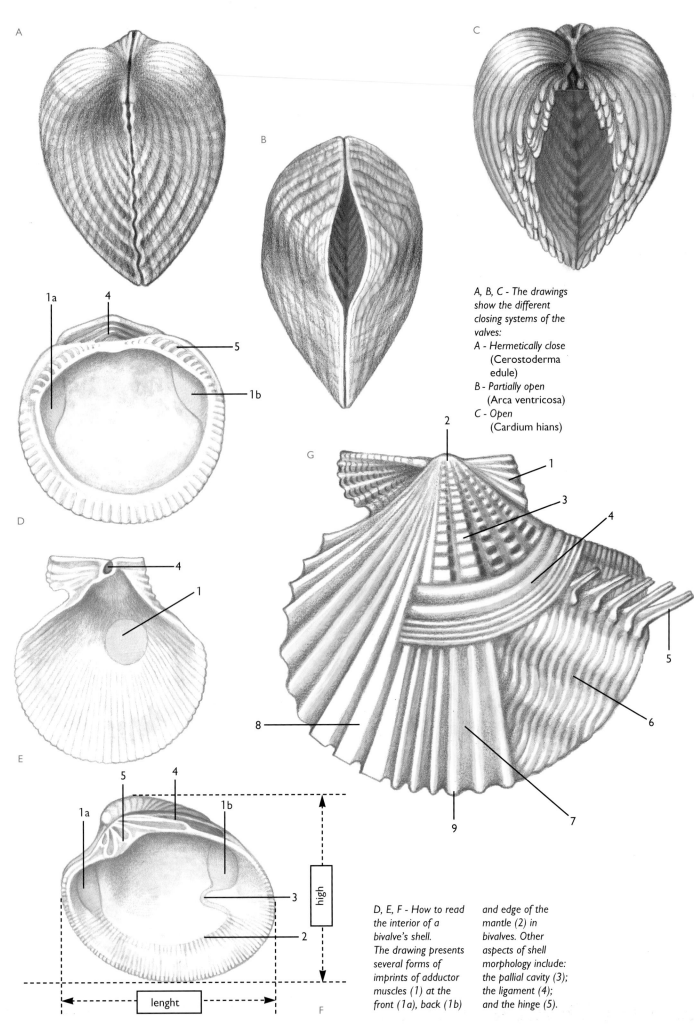

A, B, C - The drawings show the different closing systems of the valves:
A - Hermetically close (Cerostoderma edule)
B - Partially open (Arca ventricosa)
C - Open (Cardium hians)

D, E, F - How to read the interior of a bivalve's shell.
The drawing presents several forms of imprints of adductor muscles (1) at the front (1a), back (1b) and edge of the mantle (2) in bivalves. Other aspects of shell morphology include: the pallial cavity (3); the ligament (4); and the hinge (5).

scars. The aggression was attributed to large brachyuran crabs in the cone's territory, whose claws are tough enough to break its shell. In this case the mollusk saved itself by retracting far back into the shell in time, and the crab's claw found only a piece of inedible rock.

G - Ornamentation in bivalve shells. This hypothetical valve shows:
1 - auricle;
2 - umbo;
3 - radial ribs with scales;
4 - concentric ribs and stripes;
5 - spines;
6 - oblique ornamentation;
7 - radial furrows;
8 - radial ribs;
9 - ventral margin.

H - A chiton shell (nomenclature of a hypothetical polyplacophore):

1 - girdle
2 - cephalic plate
3 - posterior plate
4 - tuft of bristles
5 - median plate
6 - calcareous spines
7 - scales
8 - radial granules
9 - bristles
10 - radial ribs
11 - longitudinal ribs
12 - transverse ribs
13 - median area
14 - lateral area
15 - granules

WHERE SHELLS ARE FOUND

GEOGRAPHY OF MARINE MOLLUSKS

There are very few species of mollusks that can be considered cosmopolitan, i.e. found in all or nearly all seas of the world. Atlanta peroni, an atlantid that lives a pelagic life and swims to depths of 3000 meters, has been found everywhere. Janthina janthina, a purple snail that floats, allowing itself to be carried by the currents with plankton across the oceans, is ubiquitous, except for Arctic and Antarctic seas. A few benthic mollusks have a near planetary distribution due to the very long life of their larvae, which can cross the oceans carried by the currents. This is the case of the great trumpet shell (Charonia tritonis), which lives on rocky seabeds in all warm seas of the planet. The helmet ton (Tonna galea) also has a vast distribution, from the Mediterranean to the American coasts of the Atlantic, where it can be found from the Caribbean to the Argentine

A

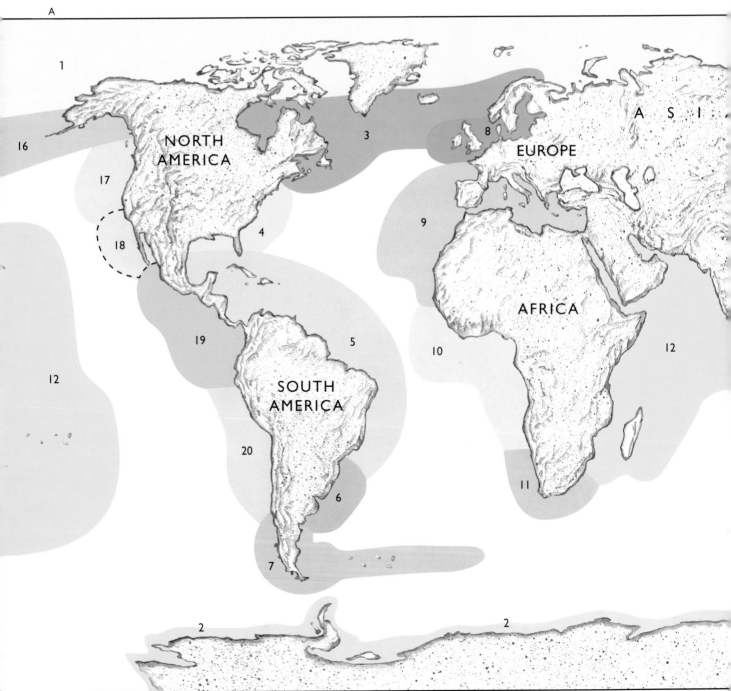

port of Mar del Plata.

Infinitely more numerous are species with a very limited geographical distribution, like an island or a small secluded body of water. These species are known as endemisms, and are the result of the well-known evolutionary phenomenon that leads to the formation of new species under conditions of geographical isolation. Thus, the island of Malta has a little top shell all its own, *Gibbula nivosa*, an elegant little snail 9 millimeters in diameter. In Polynesia, the Marquesas Islands, which have rather few shell species (170 in all) have fully 13 endemic species, from six different families.

Between the extreme cases of cosmopolitanism and endemism, the overwhelming majority of species of marine mollusks have a distribution that encompasses vast coastal areas, either delimited by geographical barriers, like continental masses, or by oceans, or by diversity in surface water temperatures. It is not so much the average annual temperature of the water that limits distribution of a species the seasonal highs and lows. Variations in climate periodically shift these extreme values, and consequently also a particular species' limits of distribution. For example, the common northern whelk (*Buccinum undatum*), an Arctic and Atlantic species, entered the Mediterranean and spread there as the sea was going through cold periods. Today its shells are found almost exclusively in the subfossil state, although a few small relict populations survive in cool, deep areas of the northwest Mediterranean.

Biogeographers have divided coastal areas of the world into about 20 malacological provinces, which are defined in such a way that no less than half the species present in each one live exclusively within its confines. In a biogeographical province, we can distinguish a center of dispersion, the area from where the majority of the species originally spread, and a metropolis, which is the area where most species currently live. The two areas may or may not be the same, depending on past environmental and biological events. Despite everything that has been said on the boundaries between one province and another, they can be nothing but very vague and temporary. There are overlapping areas, and different writers use subdivisions that differ at least in part. Subject to these special cases, we should note that most shell species are quite stable over time. In fossiliferous coastal areas, we find essentially the same fauna that live in the nearby seas.

For each species, the area of diffusion, or geographical distribution, is the result of events occurring over many hundreds of thousands of years, during which environmental conditions evolved and the biological capacity of the species developed to adapt to new conditions and occupy new territories. In the last century and a half, man has greatly interfered with this natural process, both voluntarily, by cultivating mollusks from distant seas, and involuntarily, by accidentally transporting larvae and adults while fishing and in maritime traffic. Perhaps the most notorious case was opening the Isthmus of Suez, which caused a flow of mollusks from the Red Sea to the Mediterranean that has increased over recent years, following the decreased salinity of the Bitter Lakes halfway up the Canal, which had until then constituted a biological barrier. Today there many dozen of these so-called lessepsian species, named after the man who built the Canal, the Frenchman Ferdinand de Lesseps.

JAPAN

AUSTRALIA

NEW ZEALAND

B

A - The drawing shows the 20 malacological provinces:

1 - Arctic
2 - Antarctic
3 - Boreal
4 - Transatlantic (or Carolinian)
5 - Caribbean
6 - Patagonian (or Argentinian)
7 - Magellanic
8 - Celtic
9 - Mediterranean
10 - African
11 - South African
12 - Indopacific
13 - Australian
14 - New Zealand
15 - Japanese

16 - Aleutian
17 - Oregon
18 - Californian
19 - Panamic
20 - Peruvian

B – Reefs, which can only form in the clear waters of the intertropical zone, are home to a wide range of shell species.

C - The cameo shell, Cypraeacassis rufa lives near reefs across most of the Indo-Pacific province.

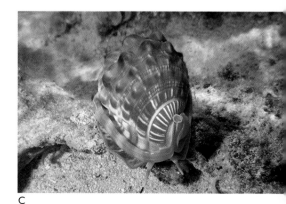

C

TROPICAL PROVINCES

A - The coastline of the tropical malacological provinces have characteristics similar to the coasts of temperate provinces, with two important exceptions: the coral reef and its immediate surroundings, and the mangrove forest. The photo shows Tahiti, a high island of volcanic origins, with its coast rimmed by the coral reef. It is part of the Indopacific province.

B - The white beach of the island of Sipadan. It is part of Sarawak, in northern Borneo, under Malaysian governance. An Indopacific province.

A

B

C

D

E

F

G

H

Indopacific. This is one of the largest provinces, and has the greatest wealth of species: it extends for three quarters of the Equator, from the west coast of Africa to the Hawaiian Islands, going through southern Asia and northern Australia. It is also the most popular among collectors throughout the world, due to the wealth of beautiful, colorful shells. The metropolis of the Indopacific province is the Indonesian archipelago, while the center of dispersion is considered the Philippine archipelago (which at present has no fewer than 5000 species), along with the whole band of archipelagos running from the Ryukyu Islands in the far south of Japan to the Great Barrier Reef of Australia.

West Africa. It has relatively few species, for several reasons which include the fact that the Atlantic coast of Africa does not have a great variety of biotopes, and is lacking in areas sheltered from sea storms. Nevertheless, its exploration is by no means complete, and probably new species will be found in the future. It is delimited to the north by Cape Blanc and to the south by Moamedes, and thus has a rather limited extension due to the cold currents and rising deep waters. Two families are particularly well represented: the margin shells, or marginellas, with dozens of beautiful species, and the volutes, with about a dozen species from the genus *Cymbium*.

Caribbean. Runs from the Florida Keys, little islands to the extreme south of Florida, to Rio de Janeiro. Its environments vary greatly (from coral reefs to mangrove muds, to vast sandy areas in sheltered environments) and has a wealth of species that, distributed over a wide expanse of territory, also include a multitude of subspecies, races and varieties. The Pleurotomaridae family is well-represented, with about a dozen species of these primitive gastropods. Particularly beautiful are the Strombidae, with the especially elegant and uncommon Strombus gallus.

Panamic. Extending from the Gulf of California to Ecuador, including the Galapagos Islands, this stretch of the Pacific American coast only has a few species in common with the Indopacific province: a few have reached the Galapagos or remote Clipperton Island, but they have not yet landed on the continent. Panamic shells do, however, have ascendants in common with species in the Caribbean province, because during the Tertiary period, before the beginning of the Pliocene, the Isthmus of Panama was open and the Gulf of Mexico and the Pacific Ocean were connected. Various shells from the two provinces are thus paired, like the two cowries, the Panamic *Cypraea zebra* and the Caribbean *Cypraea cervinetta*, descendants from a common Tertiary period ancestor. The Panamic province abounds in interesting miters, augers and cones. Collectors prize the shells of the murex Muricanthus radix, which reaches 15 centimeters in height, with rich ornamentation in the form of white and black bands.

C - The Maldive Islands, a true paradise for divers. Their clear waters are home to a rich shell population. Indopacific province.

D - Sand Island in Key West, the southern tip of Florida. Caribbean province.

E - The coast of Guadalupe Island at Pointe des Chateaux. Caribbean province.

F - Kauai, an island in the Hawaiian archipelago, of volcanic origin. Indopacific province.

G - The emerged land is desert, but the sea along it is rich in life. This is the coast of Shadwan Island, in the Red Sea. Indopacific province.

H - Coast with mangrove vegetation on Grand Comoro Island in the Indopacific.

A

C

Japan. Includes the Japanese archipelago (except for the southernmost minor islands) and the east coast of Korea, plus a short stretch of coast in the Russian province of the Far East. It has a wealth of species (over 5000) and many extremely fascinating shells. It includes rare slit shells, two turbinids, *Guildfordia triumphans* and *Guildfordia joka*, with their lovely appendages, and the great deep water turrid Thatcheria mirabilis, known as the Japanese wonder shell, with an extraordinary ladder-like form that makes it one of the most coveted shells of all.

Aleutian. Runs across the Pacific, from the northwest coast of America and the northeast coast of Asia, including the Aleutian archipelago and Sakhalin Island. Here there is an abundance of species from the genera *Trophon, Littorina,* and *Patinopecten*. A

characteristic species is the abalone Haliotis kamtschatkana, with its thin shell that may be over 15 centimeters long. It is hunted by the sea otter, which uses rocks to break its shell. The bivalves include a gigantic iatellid, *Panopea generosa*, which may weigh 4 kilos and has a shell up to 23 centimeters long. It buries itself over a meter deep in the substratum. Its very long siphons, which make up about half the animal's weight, cannot be retracted.

Mediterranean. Includes the Atlantic coast from Brittany to Cape Blanc, the Azores, the Canary Islands, Madera and the entire Mediterranean, including the Black Sea. Shells are of the warm temperate and in part subtropical type in the Atlantic south of the Strait of Gibraltar (known as the Mauritanian Region) and cold temperate with a few northern features to the north (the Portuguese Region). Depending on the climate phase, the Mediterranean basin has been populated by Atlantic fauna from one or the other of these two regions. When, as in the current phase, temperate-warm conditions prevailed, cold water shells became extinct or took refuge in deep areas. The Mediterranean is full of endemisms. Among the most characteristic shells are the cowry Luria lurida, the purple dye murex Bolinus brandaris, from which the Phoenicians obtained their famous purple dye, the pilgrim's clam or common scallop *(Pecten jacobaeus)*, the pelican's foot shell *Aporrhais pespelecani* (also common in the North Atlantic), and the Mediterranean rugose (spiny) bonnet Cassidaria echinophora.

Celtic. Includes the British Isles and continental coasts along the English Channel, the North Sea and the Baltic. Some of the more characteristic and frequent shells include the common periwinkle *(Littorina littorea),* which is gathered for

food, the whelks *Buccinum undatum* and *Neptunea antiqua*, and the murices *Nucella lapillus* and Patella vulgata. In the fjords, we may find the acmeid *Acmaea testudinalis*. On muddy seabeds the tellin *Macoma baltica* is extremely common.

Boreal. Straddles the North Atlantic, extending from the western coast of Norway to the southern coast of Iceland and Greenland, to the northeast coast of America that runs from Cape Cod to Labrador. Generally speaking, cold water shells are not as brightly colored, and for a long time collectors ignored them, but in the far north of the Atlantic there are also large species with elegant shells, like the wentletrap *Epitonium groenlandicum*, beautiful turrids from the genus *Bela,* lovely murices from the genus *Trophon,* and large whelks like *Colus islandicus*.

Transatlantic (or Carolinian). Includes the coast of North America from Cape Cod to South Florida. Common among the bivalves are the large, thick-shelled venerids k nown as

B

D

quahogs from the genus Mercenaria, which are gathered for food, the pholadid *Cyrtopleura costata,* and the iatellid *Panopea bitruncata.* The gastropods include the melongenid *Busycon carica* and the whelk *Neptunea decemcostata.*

Californian. Encompasses the American Pacific coast from British Columbia in Canada to the Baja California peninsula. Some writers recognize a separate Oregon province between the California and the Aleutian provinces. The most noteworthy shells in the area are certainly the large haliotids or abalones, with their amazing iridescence. After indiscriminate fishing for food purposes threatened their populations, their harvesting was limited by law. There are also more than 50 species of chitons and a good variety of murices.

New Zealand. Despite its relative proximity to Australia, the New Zealand archipelago has few species of mollusks in common with the coast of the continent. Of the fifty or

so species of chitons, the most noteworthy is *Eudoxochiton nobilis,* which may be 8 centimeters long, and the strange butterfly chiton, *Cryptoconchus porosus,* 15 centimeters long. Among the most beautiful and sought-after gastropods of New Zealand shells are about twenty species of volutids. Along with the precious mother-of-pearl of the abalone, with its particularly bright green iridescence (paua), they are used to make costume jewelry and real gems.

C - The seas of Sardinia, in the center of the western basin of the Mediterranean, are home to a vast number of shells from the Mediterranean province.

D – Aerial view of the vast beaches in the region of Cape Cod, in Massachusetts (USA).

E - A spectacular rocky formation at the southern tip of the Baja California peninsula in Mexico. This is where the temperate California and the tropical Panamic provinces meet.

E

71

Australian. The northern part of the continent is part of the Indopacific tropical province. The southern coast, running from Brisbane in Queensland to Geraldton in Western Australia, and the island of Tasmania, are bathed by temperate waters, with a wealth of beautiful shell species. Some of the most characteristic include the potamidid *Pyrazus ebeninus*, which populates the muddy expanses of estuaries in incredible numbers, and a living fossil, the great cerithid *Campanile symbolicum*, which vanished in Europe and Asia millions of years ago and now is found in the fossil state.

South African. Includes all of South Africa except Natal and including Namibia. Despite the relatively cool water, there is a wealth of beautiful cowries. One of the rarer finds is the slit shell Pleurotomaria africana. There are over twenty species of limpets, including some large and highly prized cones and turbos.

Patagonian (or Argentinian). Extends from Rio de Janeiro to the northern coasts of Tierra del Fuego. It has only rather recently been explored for shells, and research is far from complete. Only now are books being published for shell collectors in this area,

who have had very little material available in the past. Large volutes live in the circumlittoral areas, and are occasionally collected by Russian trawl fishing boats. Among these are the rare Voluta ferussacii, up to 10 centimeters long, and the even rarer and more coveted Voluta palliata, 9 centimeters long.

Peruvian. Runs from Ecuador to southern Chile. One of its murices, Concholepas concholepas, is very well-known, with a strange form that makes it look like an abalone. It lives in the intertidal area. It is a protected species: overharvesting for food purposes (it was sold as a delicacy known as loco) caused its disappearance from entire stretches of coast. Some of the most interesting shells in the area include a large triton, *Fusitriton magellanicus*.

Magellanic. Forms various sub-regions, with the southern tip of South America, the island of Chiloè, Tierra del Fuego, the Falkland Islands, Southern Georgia and the subantarctic archipelagos. The intertidal areas of the ice-free coasts are home to mussels like Brachidontes purpuratus and *Mytilus chilensis*, and farther down Aulacomya atra, which may be 16 centimeters in length. In the infralittoral band, mollusk fauna diversifies, with representatives from numerous families.

A

A – In the image we can see a stretch of the rocky coast of Tasmania. Rich in life, the coastal waters of this large island are part of the Australian province.

B - A sickle of beach across from the shallow sea bed of an inlet in the Falkland Islands. Along with the extreme south of the South American continent and other subantarctic islands, the archipelago is part of the Magellanic province of cool temperate waters.

B

D

could be home to populations of fragile mollusks. Yet about eighty conchiferous mollusks have been found along the coasts of Adelaide Land alone. The limpet *Laevilitorina antartica* is a summer resident in the midlittoral band, invaded by glaciers for ten months a year. Farther below, in the upper infralittoral band, there is the eatoniellid *Eatoniella kerguelensis*. Ten meters below is the muricid *Neobuccinun eatoni*. In the circumlittoral band, below 25-30 meters in depth, there are still herbivore species who feed on rhodoficious algae, with little need of light, while farther down there are carnivorous and necrophagous species who extend to hundreds of meters in depth.

C, D, E - Three aspects of the Alaskan coast near the Bering Strait. The mechanical action of the glaciers makes a permanent settlement of mollusks impossible in the tidal area. Nevertheless, some species live in the infralittoral zone and migrate higher up when the coast is temporarily freed of its icy mantle. At greater depths, there are few species of shells, although in some areas the populations are quite dense. This is the Arctic malacological province.

F - The waters of port Lockroy in Antartide, still locked in by ice. The Antarctic malacological province has been studied over recent decades and is not yet well known. The waters around the continent of ice are nevertheless very abundant in life, and mollusks are also represented with more species than was once thought.

COLD WATER PROVINCES

Arctic. The Canadian, Northern European and Siberian coasts bathed by the Arctic Ocean have no mollusks in the midlittoral band due to the abrasive action of ice. In the infralittoral and circumlittoral, there are malacological species with brownish or whitish shells, generally covered by a thick dark periostracum. The predominant bivalves include species from the genera *Yoldia, Nuculana, Hiatella* and *Mya,* while the most frequent gastropods are from the genera Buccinum, Colus, Margarites and Trophon. Of all malacological provinces, this is considered the most impoverished, with less than 400 known species.

Antarctica. It is difficult to imagine how the coasts of the continent of ice

E

F

73

THE SALT WATER REALMS

Where there's sea there are shells: there is no coast, abyss or stretch of open sea that does not include a population of mollusks. With two exceptions: the band of polar coasts regularly occupied by permanent glaciers, and pebbly, wave-swept beaches. In both these cases, mechanical forces prevent larvae from settling and adults from surviving. But in polar regions where glaciers are seasonal, mollusks occupy stretches of coast that are temporarily ice-free; and bold little snails come to pebbly beaches during periods of great summer calm, ready to flee as soon as the sea grows rough.

Marine biology breaks the sea down into various environments: a fundamental distinction is between the benthos and the pelagos. Organisms that live in close connection with the seabed, either buried or firmly adhered, or who depend on it for food and crawl over it or swim just above it, without ever going far from it, are part of the benthos, and are referred to as benthic. The overwhelming majority of mollusks with shells are benthic.

Organisms that live in open water and do not depend on the seabed or

1

High tide

2

Low Tide

3

A - Clusters of mytilids (this is the subspecies chilensis *from the cosmopolitan* Mytilis edulis, *the Atlantic mussel), left high and dry by the low tide, at West point Island in the Falklands archipelago.*

We know that the shell with its hermetic seal allows the mussel to spend many days underwtare with no problem, especially is the temperature is cool as in this sunantarctic region.

A

the organisms that populate it for their vital functions, are known as pelagic. In its turn, the pelagos can be broken down into plankton, which is formed of organisms that move with the masses of water, and nekton, which is the group of animals capable of moving freely even against the movement of the water.

Anyone studying shells needs to have a clear idea of the various areas into which the benthic domain can be broken down. The first distinction is between the littoral system, which involves the seabeds where chlorophyll-producing plants

B

B - The coral reef at low tide at Vava'u, on Tongo Island in the South Pacific. In this situation, the populations of mollusks that live on the midlittoral level escape the direct rays of the sun and take shelter under the branches or coral or in crevices in the reef.

DRAWING - Four aspects of the upper levels of the littoral system. The abundance of light and oxygen-rich water encourages settlement of numerous forms of life, despite the disadvantages of fluctuations in temperature and salinity, of wave action, and, in too many areas, by the presence of pollutants due to human activity. Hundreds of species of mollusks have made it their exclusive habitat, or they visit it from deeper habitats.

C

D

4

C - The breakers of the Atlantic Ocean crash against the reef of the Glènans Islands in Brittany. The colonies of mussels, firmly anchored to the rock with very strong filaments of byssus, are not affected by them in the slightest. In fact, the mussles offer shelter to other species of mollusks and various little animals who could not otherwise withstand the waves.

5

1 Supralittoral zone. Bathed by sea spray.
2 Midlittoral zone. Between the normal high and low tide levels.
3 Infralittoral zone. From the normal low tide level to the limits of growth of marine phanerogams.
4 Circumlittoral level. Runs from the lower phanerogam limit to the chlorophyll algae limit.
5 Deep system. Runs from the chlorophyll algae limit to the bottom.

A

A - The photophilic algae of the infralittoral zone host populations of little snails in every sea of the world. It's difficult to spot them by day, because they take refuge at the base of the vegetation.

B - Competition for space is quite fierce in the infralittoral zone. A shipwreck is rapidly covered with bivalves, as seen in the photo, in addition to algae, sponges, coelenterates and other forms of life.

C - The Posidonia oceanica meadow environment marks the lower limit of the infralittoral zone in the Mediterranean. The most visible mollusks are the beautiful nacres (Pinna nobilis) shown in the photo, who use their byssus to anchor to solid parts of the sea bed. In recent years, fishing with trawl nets and indiscriminate harvesting of these mollusks have gradually reduced populations over vast areas.

D – The spectacular camouflage of the common Lopha cristagalli bivalve which lives in the shallow waters of the Indo-Pacific province.

E – Large top-shells in shallow water, in a Polynesian lagoon. This is an environment repopulated relatively recently, in that the last glaciation had caused the total extinction of its malacofauna.

B

C

D

the transparency of the water. Where it is extremely clear, there is enough light to support plant growth even at 45 meters deep, while in murky water the limit is 8-10 meters. Finally, the lowest level of the littoral system is the circumlittoral, which, as we have noted, descends to the lowest point where chlorophyll-producing algae can still grow.

Almost all shells of interest to collectors come from these four levels of the littoral system, which can be explored without too much difficulty. Exploration of the first two requires truly minimal equipment, the third can be examined during normal scuba diving expeditions, while the fourth level, the circumlittoral, would require very difficult dives, and thus shells must be collected by professional fishermen with trawls.

The deep sea, where there is no light or chlorophyll-producing plants and organisms depend almost entirely on the snow of organic material from the pelagic domain, is the realm of scientific research. The system can be broken down into three levels. The first is the bathyal, which generally corresponds to the continental slope, which runs from the edge of the continental shelf, at an average depth of 200 meters, and drops rather abruptly to 1,500-2500 meters. The next level is the abyssal, formed of vast, rather flat areas, which may nevertheless be interrupted by underwater peaks and mountain ranges, gradually descending to about 6000 meters from the continental slope. Finally, there is the hadal level, which includes oceanic trenches that can reach depths of 11,000 meters or so.

In the benthic domain, the physical nature of the substratum is of vital ecological importance. In fact, it plays a major role in the formation of particular biocenoses, i.e. groups of living organisms bound by reciprocal dependence. Almost all mollusks are restricted to a particular type of substratum. In other words, it makes no sense to look for sandy or muddy seabed shells in a rocky environment (the case is a little different for washed-up shells: the currents and waves that carry them to shore may have taken them from various environments and then mixed them).

Later on, we will examine in detail some interesting environments for the study of shells. For now,

we'll make one important distinction, between fixed and mobile substrata. Of course, this distinction should be considered in relationship to what animal organisms need to live. For mollusks, this includes fixed substrata, not only rocks and towers of large masses, but also objects that seem mobile to us, like the chains of anchors, the hulls of boats, and the shells of various animals, while mobile substrata include sand, mud, organic detritus, and shingles, including large pebbles, in areas where the wave action rolls them. In a very sheltered cavity, those same pebbles could become a hard substratum and could become home to fauna similar to that found on reefs.

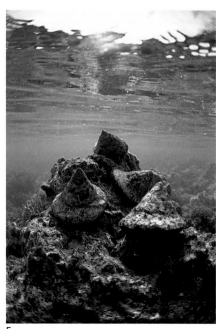

E

can grow, and the deep system, which extends beyond the limit of chlorophyll-producing vegetation.

In its turn, the littoral system is divided into four levels. Going from top to bottom, the first level is the supralittoral band, whose upper limit is where ocean spray regularly reaches, with a lower limit marked by wave movement of normal intensity during high tide. Lower down is the midlittoral band, also known as the intertidal or tidal area. Its upper limit is marked by the line that waves regularly reach during high tide, while the lower limit is the average low tide mark for normal tides. The third level of the littoral system is known as the infralittoral band: it runs from the lower edge of the midlittoral to the lowest point where phanerogamic marine plants can grow. Along the coasts of Europe, these are meadows of Zostera, and, in the Mediterranean in particular, Posidonia oceanica, the deepest growing salt water plant. On average, Zostera grows to 25-30 meters deep, but much depends on

A

ON COASTAL ROCKS

The breakers crash against the rock wall, columns of foam fly skyward with the roar of thunder. Under these hammer strokes, even the hardest rock is eroded, and in time, even the hugest cliffs crumble. We humans look on fearfully. Even the strongest swimmer would have to struggle to come out alive from that white inferno. Yet this environment, seemingly so hostile to life, is populated by an extraordinary quantity of animal and plant species and is preferred by many species of mollusks. In fact, it may be the environment in which primitive mollusks evolved. But what elements of coastal rock are favorable to marine life? There are many - many more than we would expect. Protrusions and crevices, cracks and caves, create alternating areas of bright light and shadow, exposed areas and sheltered areas. Where there is light there is vegetation, and thus food, from a thin blackish pellicle of lichens above, to rich meadows of algae below, in areas less exposed to wave motion. Shade, on the other hand, offers protection from predators.

Another gift of the rocky coast is the abundance of oxygen, which wave motion continuously dissolves in the

A - A lovely view of dusk on the emerging reef at Point Pinos near Pacific Grove, California.

Drawing, B – In the Venice lagoon the tidal range is about one metre. The drawing shows in a schematic form (for illustrative purposes, the proportions are not real) the population of a

platform above the high tide (HT) level, in the midlittoral and under the low tide (LT) level.
1 – Melaraphe neritoides
2 – Liyia
3 – Crab (Pachigrapshus)
4 - Barnacle (Chtalamus)
5 - Patella
6 - Littorina saxatilis
7 - Chiton

8 - Barnacle (Balanus)
9 - Oyster (Ostrea edulis)
10 - Mussel (Mytilus galloprovincialis)
11 - Crab (Carcinus)
12 - Prawn (Palaemon elegans)
13 - Alga (Enteromorpha)
14 - Alga (Porphyria)
16 - Alga (Ulva)
17 - Alga (Ceramium)
18 - Alga (Gracilaria)

C - Tidal pools on the Crozon peninsula in Brittany, are frequented by many mollusk species.

D - This colony of Mytilus californianus has settled along the northwest coast of the United States. Nevertheless, appearances can be deceiving: hidden by the mass of bivalves, a deep fissure furrows the rock.

B

C

D

water. There is also a great deal of suspended organic material, as all detritus that floats on the sea is tossed here. There is also a variety of dissolved salts, including those of terrestrial origin, carried by the rainwater that flows into the sea. Finally, there is the rock itself. Don't be deceived by its forbidding appearance; it helps those who can help themselves. First of all, it provides a solid anchorage. And when it is calcareous, it even allows some species of mollusks to dig tunnels where they can live a completely tranquil, albeit highly cloistered life.

The reef area which is subject to alternating tides and wave motion has seen the evolution of species capable of firmly adhering themselves. Limpets, chitons, abalone and even, in the cold waters of Chile and Peru, the murex Concholepas concholepas do this through a sort of temporary sticking action that resembles a suction cup but is not. This ability to anchor themselves allows properly equipped gastropod mollusks to alternate periods of immobility, especially when the sea is rough, with movement in search of food, especially at night. Other means of anchoring include the byssus, a bundle of robust horny or chitinous threads secreted by the mollusk's foot and affixed to the rock. The most well-known example is the mussel. The extreme solution is to adhere to the reef using a sort of cement, as do the vermetids, gastropod

A

B

mollusks that have transformed their snail-like shell into a tube similar to sedentary polychete worms, and who feed by using long, filamentous appendages to capture detritus suspended in the water. Cirriped crustaceans use the same method.

On the rocky coasts, there is a great difference between populations that inhabit the various levels. The supralittoral is occasionally battered by violent waves, but normally the rock is only moistened by ocean spray. The spray collects in fissures and cracks in particular. Very few marine mollusks live permanently on this level, which is

C

actually more aerial than aquatic, and seems better for creatures with lungs that can take in oxygen directly from the air. Most species of mollusks in this environment use their gills to breathe the oxygen dissolved in the little water that arrives with the spray, which they can conserve for long periods within their shell. The environment is also subject to great fluctuations in temperature and salinity, depending on the time of day and the season. For this reason, it is a practical habitat only for species who are highly adaptable.

The first living beings that spring into view, however, are not mollusks, but immobile cirripeds, commonly called barnacles (Chthamalus stellatus), who use their little cones cemented to the rock to encrust vast areas. No one would call them even distant relatives of another crustacean that frequents this level, the highly mobile runner or marbled crab (Pachygrapsus marmoraturs). With a little attention, we can see that, especially along fissures on European reefs, there are massive populations of a very dark, tiny little snail, 3 or 4 millimeters in height, the limpet Melaraphe neritoides. It can live in a dry environment for long periods, because its branchial chamber also acts as a very simplified lung. Still, it needs to deposit its eggs in water. The eggs are enclosed in planktonic egg capsules, which produce swimming veliger larvae. The snail keeps the egg capsule in the oviduct until the sea rises to the level of the rock it inhabits, which in the Atlantic occurs twice a year, during the great equinox tides. On the African shore of the Mediterranean and in Sicily, the lighter Nodolittorina punctata is common, up to 15 millimeters in height and adorned with little bands of white and brown dots. Littorina saxatilis, up to 16 millimeters high, can be seen on the Atlantic coast of Europe in the supralittoral band, but is usually more common in the lower level. This little

snail also tolerates a dry environment quite well, and as it is viviparous, it does not need to immerse itself in water to deposit its eggs. On the coasts of the supralittoral band of the Mediterranean, you may sometimes see the Portuguese limpet (Patella rustica), only in very sheltered areas, as well as a trochid, the common trumpet (Osilinus turbinatus), which lives only in the fissures, and a chiton, Chiton olivaceus. All these mollusks feed by grazing on the algae that forms on the reefs.

In the supralittoral band, the reef pool environment is very interesting. Reef pools are small or large cavities that form where the slope and nature of the rock allow it, and are periodically filled with salt water through the more violent waves. During sunny periods when the sea is calm, the pools dry out, becoming a salty crust, while during heavy rains and over time the salt is washed away and the pools become fresh or brackish water. In the Mediterranean, the only mollusks that frequent this very changeable micro-environment are periwinkles, while in the tropics there may also be nerites, dove-shells and purpuras.

The next level, the midlittoral, is much richer in life. Where tides are modest, this band only has an average height of 30-60 centimeters, but this may increase to many meters along

A - Competition for a place in the sun: limpets and acorn barnacles contend for space on a reef off the coast of Devon, England. Nevertheless, the mollusks are not in competition for food with these arthopods. In fact, limpets graze on the pellicle of algae that grows on rocks, while acorn barnacles use their tufts to capture suspended food particles in the water.

B - The low tide reveals a rich colony of oysters in these tidal pools on Monte Bellos Island in western Australia.

C - A tidal pool in the Pacific Rim National Park in the Canadian province of British Columbia. The shallow sea beds of this coast are extraordinarily rich in life, so much so that it is difficult to spot open patches of substratum.

D - In the midlittoral zone of this reef in the American Northwest, mussels (Mytilus californianus) and acorn barnacles (Semibalanus cariosus) compete for room and to some extent food, as the two species feed on suspended particles. Nevertheless, these waters are rich in nutrients.

D

coasts with heavy tides. Its surface area obviously depends on the slope of the rocks. If it is gentle, and if the surface of the rock is rough, tidal pools form, which are a much more stable and lively environment than the rock pools described above.

There are a great many mollusks at this level, both in species and in individuals. In addition, because this area can be easily explored with minimal equipment when the sea is calm, it is one of the most profitable in terms of observing and collecting shells. It is not a homogenous area, not even where it is very shallow. There is an upper area, bathed primarily by wave motion, and a lower area, which is almost always submerged, at least for part of the day. The upper band is frequented by periwinkles characteristic of the supralittoral band, when they periodically descend to damper environments. In Atlantic Europe, this is the preferred foraging ground for Littorina saxatilis (which also lives along the coasts of North America from Seattle to New Jersey, with an isolated population in the lagoons of Venice as well); there is also Littorina littorea, large and edible (up to 26 millimeters high, it is known as bigorneau in French restaurants and periwinkle in English ones). In the Mediterranean, this is the favorite area of two very common trochids, the common trumpet (Osilinus turbinatus), more frequent on rocks exposed to waves, and the tessellate trumpet (Osilinus articulatus), which prefers more sheltered environments. Vast

populations of these snails can be seen in just a few square meters of reef. Here we begin to see a few limpets, especially the China limpet (Patella rustica), which is distinguished from other limpets primarily because it is less flat and is adorned by little black dots. Actually the giant limpet (Patella ferruginea) is most characteristic of the midlittoral band. It is larger, with a beautiful pattern of radial, rust-colored ribs, sometimes so accentuated that it appears stellate. But overharvesting has caused it to virtually disappear from the coast of continental Italy and made it very rare even in the few areas where it survives, in the islands of the Tuscan archipelago and Sardinia. Fortunately, it is still numerous along the coasts of Algeria and Morocco. Along the American coast of the Pacific, the midlittoral band is frequented by the large black abalone (Haliotis cracherodi), which was also overharvested for a long time and is now protected, as are other abalones of the California province.

For vast areas of coast throughout the world, especially in cold seas, the lower midlittoral rock level is inhabited by large populations of mussels. As is known, mussels colonize any solid substratum, even artificial, like wharves, piers, hulls of boats, and anywhere they can anchor with their byssus. This characteristic adaptability has permitted large-scale commercial cultivation. As early as Roman times, the common mussel (Mytilus galloprovincialis) and the Atlantic mussel (Mytilus edulis) were cultivated. Mussels are filterers and, although they colonize

large stretches of reef when the sea is clean, they prefer polluted environments with a wealth of suspended organic material. This is an excellent reason to avoid gathering them in nature for food purposes (which is also prohibited by Italian law). On the Atlantic coasts of Europe and North America, mussels and cirripeds are the prey of a murex, Nucella lapillus, which in the past was harvested for its indelible purple dye, used in laundries to mark fabrics. In warmer waters, midlittoral rocks are home to populations of elegant cones like Conus californicus, from central California to Mexico.

Among the most interesting facies (associations of living beings characterized by an individual dominant species) of the lower midlittoral band is the trottoir (literally sidewalk) formed by a very solid mass of calcareous algae, primarily from the genus Lithophyllum, that has a shelf form up to a meter thick and two meters wide. Full of cracks and perforated in every direction, the trottoir retains moisture even at low tide, and its mollusk population is quite varied. In the Mediterranean this is one of the favorite habitats of the Portuguese limpet (Patella ulyssiponensis) and a chiton, Lepidochitona corrugata, which can easily be observed living on the surface of the trottoir. Within the concretions is the fragile, whitish and rather rare little snail, Fossarus ambiguus, of the Fossaridae family, the little Trimusculus mammillaris, which looks like a limpet but is very distant in evolutionary terms (it was considered a marine pulmonate until the 1975 creation of the Divasibranchs subclass, to which it was ascribed along with another limpet-shaped former pulmonate from the Mediterranean, the false limpet *Siphonaria pectinata)*, and another tiny, pink-toned bivalve no more than three millimeters high, *Lasaea rubra (Laseidae* family), which has the peculiarity of being ovoviviparous: the young leave the mother's shell when they are about half her size. The above are small shells that experts in nomenclature have had to study a great deal, often changing their names. For collectors, it is difficult to keep track of these changes, but it's necessary if we want to trace drawings and photos from books that may be somewhat dated, but are needed to identify our finds.

In different environments of the lower midlittoral level, there are various species that usually prefer the infralittoral band, which is always underwater unless there is an exceptionally low tide. The common limpet *(Patella caerulea)* is very frequent in the Mediterranean, and is one of the most interesting in its variety of forms and iridescent shell. In calm water, the shell is thin, with a very regular oval form and narrow radial ribs, while in rougher water, the shell becomes sturdier and the ribs become sparser and more accentuated, giving the shell a stellate form. In the past, malacologists believed these forms were distinct species, and even gave the shell about fifty different scientific names. A collector can put together an elegant

series of caerulea without detaching even one, just by going to the edge of the rocks and collecting those that died naturally and were cleaned by fish and other necrophagous animals. Patella vulgata is quite common in this environment in the Atlantic; it is larger (up to a diameter of 70 millimeters), more clearly conical and much less variable in form and color. If you want to examine a living limpet, you must detach it from the rock without hurting it. This operation requires some skill; wait until the mollusk lifts the edge of the shell a millimeter from the rock, and then insert a thin blade and press it with a quick rotating movement, which will prevent the limpet from reacting and adhering to the substratum. If you are not fast enough, the snail's foot will adhere to

From the conservation perspective, the reef is one of the marine environments most sensitive to the activity of man. The indiscriminate collection of animal species certainly plays a significant role. Another worrisome element is pollution from hydrocarbons dumped into the sea either through carelessness or as a result of oil tanker spills. The oil slicks that mar stretches of reef along the coasts of all seas remind us that controls of this high environmental risk activity are far from effective. Port structures, shoreline reclamation, and even the construction of beach resorts directly on the reef upset or even destroy the fundamental prerequisites for life in the coastal environment.

D

the rock with such force that your attempt to detach it will lacerate and kill it. The limpet is a mollusk with archaic features. One that probably lived about 400 million years ago, known as *Damilina*, was found in a fossil state in Bohemia. At first glance, it might seem similar to primitive monoplacophores. But appearances are deceiving: the limpet's seeming bilateral symmetry, which can be seen by observing its horseshoe-like muscular system, proves false if you anatomically examine its internal organs, which reveal its past history as a true snail, which like others underwent a torsion of the viscera. Its return to a shield-shaped shell is an evolutionary adaptation to the reef habitat, because this form offers maximum resistance to wave motion.

A - The limestone rock in the midlittoral level to about a hundred meters deep, is home to perforating mollusks like the date mussels (Lithophaga lithophaga) in the photo, present in the Mediterranean, the Atlantic ocean and the Red Sea.

B - Examples of Trochus niloticus on a shallow sea bed on Sunday Island in the Kimberley region of western Australia.

C - A ventral view of the limpet, a gastropod that is perfectly adapted to

life on rocky, wave-battered surfaces. Visible are the broad, disk-shaped foot, which guarantees the animal very strong adhesion to the substratum, the head, the mouth, and the head and lateral tentacles.

D - A population of periwinkles in a fissure of a reed in Cornwall. Some species of this family spend much of their lives under water. They feed on the film of algae and lichens that the sea spray forms on the rocks in the supralittoral band.

C

DESCENT INTO THE SHADOWS

A

A, C - Even at a modest depth of ten or twenty meters, among the walls and below the spurs of rock, and even more so within caves, the quantity of light decreases quite rapidly. The species of algae change. In these environments, we may see mollusks that normally settle at greater depths in the coral environment.

Anyone who likes to snorkel prefers rocky seabeds that are always under water or only rarely emerge during especially low tides.

Whether you snorkel from the surface, free dive or use scuba gear, the infralittoral band offers the greatest number of species. The most spectacular show is in tropical coral reefs (discussed below), but there is no dearth of thrills in temperate water environments either.

Your gaze will be captured by fish as they elegantly glide or swiftly dart, or by less active creatures who are just as distinctive in form and color, like starfish, sea urchins, and colorful sponges. Mollusks with shells are elusive, and many are masters of

B

mimicry. Sometimes, as you begin exploring a rocky seabed in the infralittoral band, you may see only limpets and mussels. This is certainly deceiving, and gradually, as your eyes grow accustomed to the peculiarities of the underwater landscape, you may note that a small sponge is hiding the shell of the thorny oyster (Spondylus), firmly anchored to the rock, or what seemed to be a greenish clump of algae turns out to be the shell of a well-disguised murex. Not to mention the snails that play hide and seek among the algae and fissures in the rock. In this environment, experience will play an important role in what you see.

Where wave action is not particularly powerful, the underwater reef is covered with photophilic, or light-loving, algae. In

Drawing, B – The illustration shows an example of a rocky infra-coastal environment (European coastline).
The elements of the coastline, for illustrative purposes, are not in real proportions.
1 - Coris julis (male)
2 - Coris julis (female)
3 - Thalassoma pavo (female)
4 - Thalassoma pavo (male)
5 - Gibbula varia

6 - Arca noae
7 - Patella coerulea
8 - Hexaplex trunculus
9 - Haliotis lamellosa
10 - Mitra zonata
11 - Thais lacera
12 - Buccinulum corneum
13 - Spondylus gaederopus
14 - Callistoma laugieri
15 - *Alga* (Ulva)
16 - *Alga* (Codium)
17 - *Alga* (Halimeda)
18 - *Alga* (Acetabularia)
19 - *Alga* (Udotea)

C

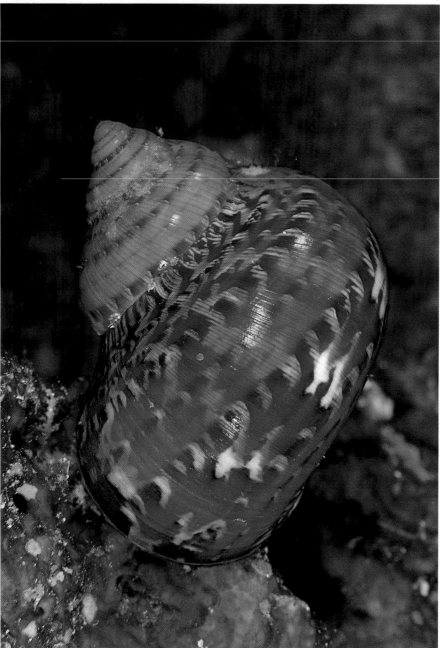

A

province, you will see murices like *Muricopsis cristata* and *Ocinebrina edwardsi*, the red-mouth purpura *(Thais lacera)*, the horn nassa *(Nassarius corniculum)*, the common whelk *(Buccinulum corneum)*, the trunculus murex *(Hexaplex trunculus)*, the sting winkle *(Ocenebra erinaceus)*, the knotty tulip *(Fasciolaria lignaria)*, the cone *Conus mediterraneus*, the mother-of-pearl top *(Gibbula richardi)*, the variegated top *(Gibbula varia)* and the concave top *(Gibbula rarilineata)*, the rock cerith *(Cerithium rupestre)*, and the beautiful rough turbo *(Bolma rugosa)*, whose calcareous operculum has been called St Lucy's eye and is considered a good luck charm by

B

A - *The turbinid (Turbo petholatus) in the coral reed of New Guinea. It is fairly common and is harvested to make ornamental objects.*

B – *Two specimens of* Turbinide astraea gibberosa, *encrusted with seaweed, on a cliff in British Columbia (Canada).*

C - *A large abalone from California,* Haliotis corrugata. *It may reach 25 centimeters in diameter and lives primarily at depths of from 6 to 10 meters.*

D - *A* Spondylus gaederopus *is camouflaged among the algae on rocky sea bed of Malta.*

E - *The murex (Urosalpinx cinerea), 4 centimeters long, hunting on a sea bed in California.*

this environment, populations of mobile mollusks can be broken down into three groups. The first includes mollusks that are in general quite small and prefer living on the thalli of algae (we'll talk about them in the chapter on mollusks of underwater meadows), dropping to the sea floor and seeking shelter in the cracks of the rock only when disturbed. The second includes those who graze on the rocks, even during broad daylight, while the third group comprises those who stay in the shadows during the day and move to open areas only at night.

An extraordinary number of shell species live in these seas. As an example, in well-lighted environments in the Mediterranean

fishermen. A number of gastropods live cemented to the substratum in this environment, including the vermetids *Vermetus cristatus*, *Petaloconchus glomeratus* and *Serpulorbis arenaria*, who during the course of evolution lost their spiral-shaped shell and took on the worm-like appearance that gives the family its name. Limpets, who also live in the midlittoral band, inhabit this environment as well. The common limpet *(Patella caerulea)* lives up to 5 or 6 meters in depth, while the China limpet *(Patella ulyssiponensis)* lives higher up and rarely descends below three meters. Among the bivalves, the common mussel *(Mytilus galloprovincialis)*, can be found as deep as about three meters, especially in waters rich in

C

E

organic substances; the Noah's ark (Arca noae) often inhabits small cracks; and there are also large beds of flat oysters (Ostrea edulis).

There are shadowy areas even just a few meters deep, where you will see species that prefer to take refuge from direct light. Some examples are the abalone Haliotis lamellosa, many trochids, including the elegant members of the Clanculus genus, Clanculus cruciatus and Clanculus jusseui, the murices Engina leucozona, the striate cantharus (Pisania striata) and Fusinus rudis; and the little horny miter (Mitra cornicula). But there are also ubiquitous species in the rocky environment that can be found on various detrital seabeds and in meadows of algae or Posidonia.

It is thrilling to enter an underwater cave for the first time. You may feel euphoric as well as a bit anxious, as the twilight of the cave is full of mystery. It's a completely different world from the bright waters just a few meters away. And this is a completely justified

D

sensation. In fact, at just a few meters deep, the lack of light radically changes the plant and animal environment. Just 3-5 meters below the surface, all that's needed is a wide rocky roof or large masses in close proximity to create plant and animal associations that are very different from the reef in full light. But in a cave, if light is dramatically less than at the surface, you will find yourself in a true deep sea environment. As the darkness gradually increases, algae grows scarce, those below the tide level vanish, and the fan-like thalli of Udotea petiolata, the prickly pear-like thalli of Halimeda tuna and the calcareous little rods of Pseudolithophillum expansum appear among the soft algae. This environment is a precursor to the coral habitat, which normally begins at a few dozens meters deep, where the green meadows of marine phanerogams can no longer grow.

Light, which the various species of algae need to grow, cuts and breaks up the infralittoral band, creating deep sea niches in relatively shallow water, depending on the plays of light and shadow created by rock formations. In this environment, a dive at a constant depth, let's say about ten meters, will allow you to explore a good variety of environments that would otherwise require much deeper dives. Mobile mollusks are less dependent than algae on changes in light, but have a marked preference for a particular environment, although it is not uncommon to see them in adjacent environments as well. Thus, the abalone (Haliotis lamellosa), the murex (Fusinus rudis), and the bivalve Cardita calcyculata prefer the infralittoral environment sheltered from direct light, but they also live in niches within the coral environment.

A very interesting association is that of mollusks with coelenterates growing in the infralittoral band. In all seas of the world, but in particular in the Caribbean and Panamic provinces, this ecological niche contains most representatives of the Epitoniidae family, the wentletrap, which include over 200 species of shells, with sculptures of unrivaled elegance. Wentletraps feed primarily on coelenterates, whose tissues they suck, wherever they find

them, including various substrata at any number of depths.

In the Mediterranean, there are over 30 species. The largest wentletrap is Epitonium magnificum from Japan, which reaches 12.5 centimeters in size. Only half as big, but much more famous in the history of shell collecting, is the lovely, pale pink precious Wentletrap, Epitonium scalare, found from southern China to the coast of Queensland, Australia.

In the 18th century it was so prestigious that it was manufactured and sold on by various Chinese counterfeiters, who were able to reproduce it using rice paste. The most coveted wentletrap in America (it lives from North Carolina to the Caribbean) is the noble wentletrap, Sthenorhytis pernobilis, whose habitat is also quite deep. From Florida to England to the Mediterranean we find Gyroscala lamellosa, which is rather common on sandy seabeds, where the coelenterate Anemonia sulcata lives. Many species of wentletraps are difficult for collectors, because they are quite hard to identify. There are two ovulids in the Indopacific: the large Ovula ovum, white with a brown aperture, and very popular with collectors, and the small Calpurnus verrucosus.They both live in the infralittoral band. At greater depths, and associated with red coral, is the ovulid Pseudosimnia carnea from the Mediterranean and Caribbean provinces; its shell ranges from pale pink to brick red. In all warm and temperate waters of the world associated with gorgonians, there are ovulids from the subfamily Simniinae. They generally assume the color of the coelenterates on which they feed. They are tiny shells like the graceful orange Cyphoma gibbosum from the Caribbean, less than 3 centimeters in length.

ON AND UNDER THE SAND AND MUD

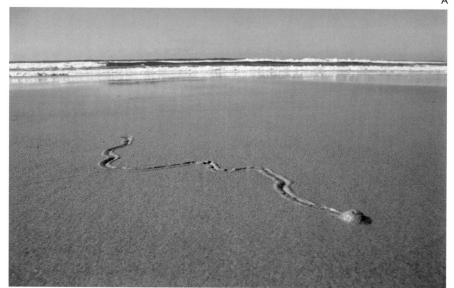

A - In Carenero in the Los Roques Islands of Venezuela, the sea has tossed an incredible number of strombid shells on the beach; these shells are abundant on shallow, sandy beds throughout the Caribbean.

B - Its sturdy foot allows this Australian moon from the genus Polinices to plow the shallow sandy bed near Wooli. Like all naticids, this snail also attacks bivalves buried in the sand by perforating its shell with its radula and then inserting its proboscis into the hole.

Drawing, C - The drawing represents schematically the population of a sandy bed of the Indo-Pacific province.
1 - Donax cuneatus
2 - Dentalium elefantinum
3 - Solen truncata
4 - Natica onca
5 - Neroitopsis radula
6 - Terebra affinis
7 - Polinices melanostomus
8 - Phalium arola
9 - Natica aracnoidea
10 - Epitonium scalare
11 - Casmaria ponderosa
12 - Lambis chiregra
13 - Conus striatus
14 - Cypraea lamarckii
15 - Cypraea pantherina
16 - Strombus
17 - Xenophora solanoid
18 - Strombus variabilis
19 - Nassarius gemmulatus
20 - Architectonica perspectiva
21 - Conus geographus (whilst devouring a fish)

C

D

Beaches are the first place that comes to mind when we think of gathering shells, but they are not necessarily ideal. Of course, in the winter, after a strong sea storm has turned the coastal seabeds upside down, you may gather a good collection of specimens that are still fresh and intact, but normally, above the high tide mark you will only find single valves of common bivalves and a few gastropod shells, broken or calcined by the sun. Of course, while these modest finds have no place in a collection, they are useful indicators of the environment on the underlying seabeds unless they are leftover food or garbage abandoned by fishing boats. At any rate, it is worthwhile to carefully observe the detritus washed up on shore, because there are areas where the currents, tides and waves bring in enormous quantities of microshells, especially if the nearby seabeds are made up of meadows of algae and phanerogams. In a sample of a liter of sand from the beach at Sfax, Tunisia, a total of 174,286 microshells was counted! In some quite particular environments, there are beaches formed only of shells, such as Shell Beach at Shark Bay Natural Park in Western Australia, where you can walk for kilometers on a layer of shells up to ten meters deep. The beach is made up solely of the valves of the little cardiid Fragum erugatum, which inhabits the bed of the opposite lagoon. The shells are blown to the beach by the wind after the surf carries them, dead and empty, to the shore.

When you go from a stretch of reef, or from various solid substrata, like a pier or wharf, to a sandy beach, you will see completely different species of shells. On beaches formed of materials that dry out quickly, like sand and shingles, no mollusks live above the high tide mark. The case is different if the materials dry out slowly, like earth mixed with rocks and decomposing plant material, found along the shores of brackish marshes, or in canals and estuary areas sheltered from wave motion. Here the humidity lasts long enough to allow mollusks to live within the crevices in the material. Of course, only mollusks with very small shells can move through this environment. In the Mediterranean these include Truncatella subcylindrica, *Ovatella myosotis, Assiminea littorina* and a few others. The fine sand on the portion of beach periodically inundated by the tide is home to a certain number of mollusk species, but there are far fewer where there is coarse sand or shingles. In the Mediterranean (but not in the Adriatic), it is not difficult to find specimens of the wedge shell *(Donacilla cornea)* by digging with your hands into the sand at the water's edge, provided the sand in the area is siliceous and not calcareous. In the intertidal area of the Adriatic, you will find the common clam (*Chamelea gallina*), two species of coquina (*Donax trunculus* and *Donax semistriatus*), known locally, and improperly, as tellins, and, since the late 1960's, an immigrant from the Indopacific region, the ark clam (*Scapharca inaequivalvis*).

But where the tide is much broader and uncovers sandy seabeds dozens or even hundreds of meters wide, as occurs along vast stretches of the French Atlantic coast, collecting mollusks, including edible species, is much more rewarding, because for the most part these bivalves are not only edible, but also particularly prized. Using shovels, rakes and other

A

B

systems refined by experience, fishermen in the area dig up the sea truffle or warty Venus (*Venus verrucosa*), the common cockle (*Cardium edule*), the dog cockle (*Glycymeris glycymeris*), the gray trough shell (*Mactra glauca*), two species of coquina (*Donax vittatus* and *variegatus*), the variegated scallop (*Chlamys varia*), the saddle oyster (*Anomia ephippium*), and the yellow razor clam (*Solen marginatus*). These species, or members of the same genera, are also found in the Mediterranean, but usually in the infralittoral band, on seabeds that are always underwater, below the low tide mark.

If you carefully observe a sandy, shallow seabed through a diving mask, it may often feel like swimming over a

desert: a few little fish, an alga, or a small hermit crab carrying a shell its builder left empty, are often the only signs of life. But appearances are deceiving. Hidden and protected by the sand is a whole universe of prey and predators from different phyla in the animal world. And mollusks with shells are well represented. For mollusks, a mobile substratum has advantages and disadvantages compared to a fixed one. It is easier to find shelter by diving into a hole and hiding there, but that hole does not provide as much protection from a predator's attack as a narrow crevice in the rock. When the sea is rough and shallow seabeds are swept by waves, a mobile substratum offers no place to anchor, and digging deeper

into the sand may not be enough. Thus, periodically the sea wreaks havoc with benthic animals and hurls immense quantities to shore.

Bivalves have chosen different strategies to populate the seabed. To eat, some species are equipped with vertical siphons that inhale water to capture plankton and suspended detritus; these are known as planktophages and suspension feeders. Other species have a siphon that works horizontally, sucking the detritus lying on the seabed, and are known as detritovores. In any case, you may often note their presence by carefully observing the surface of the sand in the infralittoral band; if you see two little holes, there will be two siphons in action. Snails that prey on bivalves leave a long, sinuous little furrow to mark their passage.

Sometimes a sandy or muddy seabed will have a very large number of bivalves, but of just a few species, while the population of predator mollusks is clearly fewer in terms of individuals, but more numerous in terms of species. Many of the more interesting gastropods for shell collectors come from sandy or muddy seabeds or those with very fine detritus. One example is Architecnonica perspectiva from the Indopacific, whose umbilicus seems designed by a whimsical architect. A large number of conch species, including the elegant *Babylonia formosae* of the West Pacific, the *Naticidae* family, great predators of bivalves, many large species from the

Cassidae family, in particular *Cassis fimbriata* (reaches 12 centimeters in length) from the Australian province, and *Cassis madagascariensis* from the Caribbean (although its name seems to indicate otherwise), and two cassids from the Indopacific, *Phalium areola* and *Phalium bandatum*, with checkerboard-design shells, are among the shells most commonly sold in souvenir shops. But the cassid in this area that played a leading role in the history of art is *Cypraecassis rufa*, a large shell (over 20 centimeters long) that has been used to make cameos since ancient times (the artist uses the difference in color between the ostracum and the hypostracum to bring the profile of the portraits into relief). Many species of beautiful murices live on

periostracum that resembles the surrounding environment. *Conus tulipa*, which lives in the sand along the Great Barrier Reef of Australia, is not as large as the notorious Conus geographus (it is no more than 7 centimeters long), but is just as poisonous, and poses a mortal danger to humans as well.

The sand of the tropics is home to some of the most beautiful representatives of the families *Harpidae, Mitridae, Costellariidae, Olividae* and *Strombidae*. Among the latter, the shells of species from the genus Lambis are spectacular for the long, arcuate digitations of their shells. They are popularly known as sea scorpions or spider shells, but their names do them an injustice; unlike most snails of mobile

one of the largest and most spectacular representatives of the family, Imperial Volute *(Cymbiola imperialis)*, which reaches 25 centimeters in length. The Bat Volute, *(Cymbiola vespertilio)* is common from the Philippines to Australia, on seabeds of sand and mud up to 20 meters deep; it takes its name from the interesting bat wing pattern on its shell. On the sandy seabeds of West Africa, from the Strait of Gibraltar to Senegal, fishing boats with trawls often come up with spectacular booty in the form of Cymbium (the species *Cymbium cymbium* may exceed 15 centimeters in length), volutes with an exceptionally wide aperture. Local populations consume the mollusk as food, while shells in good condition are sold to collectors.

D

sand, mud and detritus, like *Chicoreus cervicornis* from southern Australia and *Chicoreus spectrum* from the Caribbean.

Of the families most prized by collectors, the Conidae family is particularly well-represented on sandy or muddy seabeds in the infralittoral and circumlittoral bands. In shallow waters of the Indopacific, the multitude of species includes *Conus virgo*, which prefers muddy seabeds; *Conus zonatus* and *Conus zeylanicus*, from the Gulf of Bengal in western Indonesia, which come very close to shore. In honor of its name, *Conus leopardus* has a beautiful light shell dotted with little black spots, but when it creeps along muddy seabeds, it's very difficult to see it, because it is covered by a dark

substrata, members of the genus *Lambis* are peaceful herbivores.

On the other hand, most of the lovely, highly prized volutes are voracious carnivores. Because they have no poison glands, they are forced to approach their prey and kill it with blows of their radula, and thus have developed a very unusual characteristic among snails - speed. Those from the genus Amoria are almost exclusively from Australia, as only one or two species have reached the southernmost islands of Indonesia. This is also explained by the way volutes reproduce; they do not have a period of larval, planktonic existence, but come into the world as little snails already formed. In the Philippines, on sandy seabeds from 2 to 20 meters deep, is

A - An Atlantic scallop (Pecten maximus) on a sandy bed off the English coast: it is moving along calmly, expelling water from the valves near the hinge.

B - The two little holes in the sandy sea bed signal the presence of a buried mollusk. They are in fact the openings of the inhaling and exhaling siphons.

C - Two examples of pipi (Donax deltoides), a donax that lives in eastern and southern Australia, buried in the beds of coarse coastal sand at a depth of a few meters. We can clearly see the siphons and the foot.

D - The sandy sea beds of the Indopacific hold much satisfaction for enthusiasts. Here, the photographer has surprised a strombus, who has left evident ruts in the sand before burrowing down.

THE CORAL THEATER

A, B, D - The reef has different habitats with regard to mollusks. A diver swimming above a garden of Acropora like that of the Great Barrier Reef of Australia in the photo (A) may have the impression that the shells and their builders are absent. But this is not so: there are a myriad of mollusk species that find their ecological niche among the corals. Only the very sturdy and massive giant clams (B and D) do not mind being exposed to the sunlight.

A

Great coral reefs form only in warm seas. And there are more species of coveted mollusks in these seas than anywhere else, because here are the most beautiful and rare shells in the world. Yet a brief vacation in a tourist area near a coral reef will not necessarily provide an opportunity to see and collect a great number of species, as some places, like the lagoons in Polynesian atolls, are home to very few species. This is due to the great glaciations in the Quaternary period that lowered the sea level, transformed the lagoons into closed salt lakes and then dried them out, causing the extinction of all existing forms of life, including calm water bivalves. At the end of each glaciation, when the sea level rose and the waters once again invaded the dried-out lagoons, only the few coral reef bivalves exposed to wave motion were able to repopulate them - but it wasn't a hospitable environment for them. So sea currents had to carry a sufficient number of larvae from distant coasts for the lagoons of the atolls to once again become home to new populations of rather diversified bivalves.

Despite these periodic catastrophic events, mollusks, along with fish and corals, play an important role on the great stage of

B

C

92

Drawing, C –
A reconstruction of a stretch of the Australian Great Barrier Reef. As with the other illustrations, the various elements are not to scale for reasons of graphical clarity.

1 - Tridacna
2 - Turbo petholatus
3 - Conus imperialis
4 - Charonia trinois *whilst devouring an* Acanthaster planci *star*
5 - Pearl oyster Pteria margaritifera
6 - Cypraea vitellus
7 - Lopha folium
8 - Coralliophila costulans
9 - Haliotis orina
10 - Limaria fragilis
11 - Acanthopleura gemmata
12 - Pteria saltata
13 - Gloripallium pallium
14 - Calpurnus verrucosus
15 - Drupella cornus

D

marine life that is the reef, in all its forms. And the star is certainly the tridacna. Indeed, while other bivalves tend to hide themselves, the tridacna likes to stand out. From its open valves, we can see its brilliantly colored mantle, running from blue to green to orange to purple, often in contrast with brown or black striped or spotted patterns. The Tridacnae family lives only in the Indopacific province, with eight species, six in the genus Tridacna and two in the genus *Hippopus*. The tridacna we all know best is the giant clam *(Tridacna gigas)*, which came to Europe in the Middle Ages, when it was placed in churches as a font for holy water. Its shell may exceed 130 centimeters in length and weigh as much as 250 kilos. The first marine biologists to study it were faced with a paradox. All bivalves feed by filtering what they find in the water. But how could a gigantic bivalve live in the waters of the coral reef, which are transparent precisely because there is little suspended organic matter? The research generated by this problem led to the discovery of one of the most fascinating cases of symbiosis, involving the mollusk and single-celled zooxanthellae algae. The mollusk cultivates the algae within the tissues of its mantle, which is exposed to sunlight to permit the algae's chlorophyll-producing system to operate. The clam certainly receives oxygen and organic material from the algae, but how the exchanges between the two symbionts actually occur is still not clear. Certainly, the mollusk avoids drawing on its capital

A

B

of *zooxanthellae,* just like a good gardener who lets enough lettuce plants go to seed so he'll have enough for the next harvest. In exchange, the algae receives the giant clam's catabolites - garden compost, so to speak, plus perfect lighting in a well-protected environment. The symbiosis is perfectly analogous to what occurs between zooxanthellae and colonies of coral polyps. Among other things, by absorbing carbon dioxide, as all plants do, the algae reduce the acidity of the water, encouraging the growth of corals as well as mollusks with shells.

This type of feeding has played a role in the evolution of the tridacna, causing a 180 degree rotation of its vertical axis. Thus, unlike the clam, which stands up buried in the sand with the hinge up and the flaps of the mantle down, the tridacna lies buried stomach up among the corals, with the hinge down and the flaps of its mantle clearly visible. And what gives the tridacna's mantle its brilliant colors? It has tiny lenses of organic material known as iridocytes that it uses to set the right quantity of light for its algae, just as a gardener does when he covers or lights a greenhouse. In the past, the tridacna was collected for food: to remove it from the coral branches in which it lived buried, a large section of the coral reef had to be destroyed. Now this precious environment is treated

A, B - An enthusiast finds the best opportunities to observe shells on the infralittoral level of the coral reef, which is not difficult to visit when the sea is very calm. Nevertheless, you need to be very careful not to break branches of living coral. In A, well camouflaged formations of bivalves, anchored to a large formation of dead coral. In B, a Lopha on a branch of gorgonia.

with more respect, and tridacnas are regularly raised for their meat, shells and as living specimens for aquarium owners. Thus, you can collect them without feeling guilty, provided you have room for them in your home or aquarium.

In tropical regions, there is a clear distinction within mollusk families between species that prefer waters

D

E

C

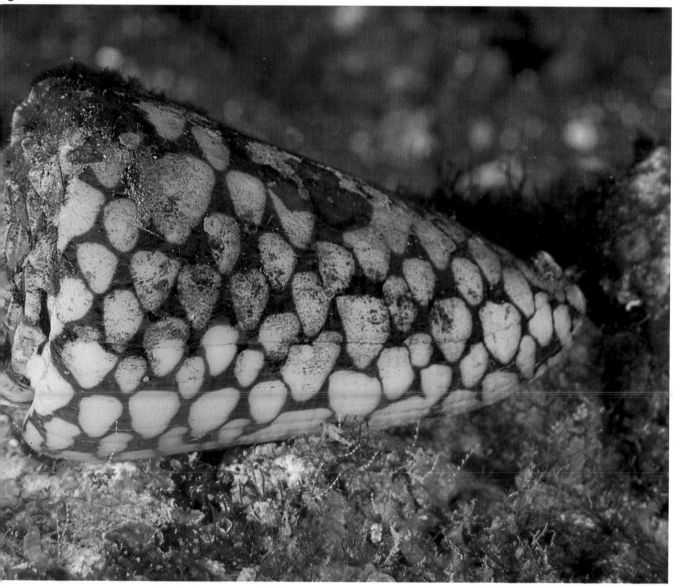

strongly affected by the proximity of continental masses, and strictly oceanic species. The mollusks that populate coral formations are for the most part members of the latter group, although corals can develop in the immediate vicinity of the coast through so-called barrier reefs, or else grow in the open sea along the edge of the continental shelf (like the Great Barrier Reef in eastern Australia). In both cases, the barriers are formed where the flow of continental waters and thus sediments is non-existent or extremely reduced (such as the Red Sea) and water conditions (variations in salinity and quantity of suspended materials) are not much different from those of coral formations in the open sea, like the ring-shaped ones

C - A large cone photographed in Bali, Conus marmoreus. It is found in the coral reeds of the Indopacific, especially, below pieces of dead coral or at the base of colonies of coelenterates. Although it feeds on

mollusks and thus does not need a potent poison like that used by others of its genus who prey on fish, there have been cases of poisoning.

D, E - Two bivalves have settled among the corals on the reef.

expansion, the area where life is richer and more abundant. In this area as well, similar to what we have noted for rocky coasts, there are differences between the fauna of the midlittoral band, which is periodically left dry by the tide, and the infralittoral band, which is almost underwater. Vagile species, however, move from one level to another, and the tidal pools of the coral reef have a wealth of beautiful shells.

On the coral reefs of the Indopacific, the large Trochus niloticus and the pearl oyster, Pinctada margaritifera, live on the outer slope. Due to their great economic importance in the production of pearls and mother-of-pearl, their populations were decimated by uncontrolled

A B

that form atolls.

The complex coral seascape includes a wide variety of substrata and exposure to light, factors that play a major role in mollusk populations. Some of the most important environments include coral sand lagoons, sometimes scattered with dead corals or dotted with isolated formations of live corals, often with a wealth of algae and phanerogamic plants; channels that connect lagoons with the open sea and are dense with coralline, encrusting algae; the maze of passages and tunnels that open within the ridge of the reef, creating microenvironments enlivened by the flow of the tide; and finally, on the slope facing the open sea, the barrier reef, which is the zone of coral

D

C

A - The image shows the thrilling encounter of a diver with a great triton (Charonia tritonis).

B - A vermetid, Serpulorbis squamigerus from California. This vermiform shell is cemented to the reef and completely hidden by sponges and algae.

C - A tiny ovulid crawls along a branch of coral. Mollusks in this family are for the most part associated with gorgonians and soft corals.

D - Well-camouflaged gastropods cling to the coral reef.

E - Tiny parasitic gastropods at work among the spines of a large sea urchin: they feed by sucking liquids from its tissue.

harvesting. Now the two species are successfully cultivated, and the natural populations are slowly recovering. The cone family is represented by beautiful species that live primarily at the foot of or in pockets of sand within coral formations. Often they are invisible due to a "camouflage suit" of encrusting coral algae or a periostracum wrapped in green algae. Others, like the *Conus nusatella* of the Indopacific, become almost impossible to reach, as they slip under various layers of dead coral. *Conus marmoreus, Conus generalis, Conus lithoglyphus,* and *Conus geographus* live in infralittoral coral sands in the Indopacific. The latter species, which hunts fish, is armed with a poison dart that may be

E

mortal even to humans. *Conus jaspideus* and *Conus daucus* live in a similar environment within coral formations in the Caribbean. The Great Barrier Reef of Australia is home to an extraordinary number of cones: *Conus lividus, flavidus* and *miles* prefer the midlittoral band, while *Conus mustellinus* is found in intertidal areas, including coral rock exposed to light.

Of all shells, the most prized are cowries. Most of the approximately two hundred species of these beautiful shells prefer a coral environment. It is very difficult to spot them during the day, but it is not uncommon to see them at night as they graze on algae around coral formations. On the outer slope of the reef in the southwest Pacific, lives the legendary golden cowry *(Cypraea aurantium),* a royal emblem in ancient Polynesia, and even now rare and highly prized. There are beautiful variations of color in the tiger cowry *(Cypraea tigris),* common in much of the Indopacific. There are even completely black specimens. They prefer to live under blocks of dead coral. Widespread in the same area, but less common, is another reef inhabitant, the eyed cowry *(Cypraea argus),* with its surface scattered with circular patterns that look like the hundred eyes of the mythological Greek monster Argus. The midlittoral band of the reef, down to two meters deep, is home to the money cowry *(Cypraea moneta),* quite common along with

the gold-ringer cowry *(Cypraea annulus),* which is also found in rocky, non-coralline environments. As we will see, these two Indopacific species, used as money, were of great importance in the international trade of pre-modern peoples. On the reefs of the Caribbean, there are only about a half dozen species of cowry. *Cypraea zebra* (which does not have a striped shell as its name might imply, but has round spots, and is in fact known as the measled cowry), has a special system for caring for its eggs.

The female spreads its mantle over them as if brooding, and periodically removes detritus from them with its proboscis. The ovulid *Volva volva* lives in the coral environment, feeding primarily on gorgonians; it has an extremely elongated form that may be as much as 10 centimeters in length.

One of the stars in coral habitats is the trumpet shell *(Charonia tritonis),* which may be as long as 45 centimeters. Widespread in other environments as well, and in warm or temperate seas around the world, it was universally used by humans as a musical instrument. But several years ago newspapers also proclaimed it the defender of the reef, as it preys on the crown-of-thorns *Acanthaster planci,* which devours coral. The uncontrolled multiplication of the crown-of-thorns was attributed to overharvesting of tritons. Now the trumpet shell is a protected species.

A - This strange formation of Posidonia oceanica meadow in the Mediterranean Sea, is due to the rhizomes, when they grow upward, to prevent the plant from being suffocated by the accumulation of detritus carried in by the currents. In this manner, tables form, among which channels and wide areas are created, moving the sea bed and encouraging the amount and variety of marine life around it.

B - A beautiful meadow of Posidonia australis, off the coast of Western Australia. This environment offers protection to many small living species, in particular the tiny snails that hide beneath the thick leaves, within the maze of rhizomes or below layers of rotting leaves, the so-called thanatoposidonia habitat.

A

B

HIDDEN IN UNDERWATER MEADOWS

When you swim over an underwater meadow, either scuba diving or snorkeling, you will see few or no shells. But if you rummage through the sand on the bank of a sheltered basin with a bed rich in vegetation, you will find an often astonishing quantity of empty shells. They are small or even tiny, most of them only a few millimeters long, almost all eroded by the surf and calcined by the sun. But there will be a few fresh ones just washed up among all these, and you'll find it worthwhile to take out a lens and observe them at your leisure, as their sculptures and colors are of a rare elegance.

They are the little inhabitants of algae and marine phanerogams, which offer perfect hiding places, making it very difficult to observe them in nature. To collect them live, the traditional technique says to pull off a tuft of vegetation from the floor and immerse it in a bucket of fresh water. The mollusks will drop to the bottom and it will be easy to collect them to put them in a aquarium and observe them at your leisure, or return them to their environment after examining and identifying them. But this procedure is not recommended for those areas of sea where meadows are at risk.

The most surprising inhabitant of these environments is Berthelina chloris, from the Juliidae family, which

Drawing, C –
The drawing shows an example of population of the underwater pasture at Posidonia oceanica in the Mediterranean (for illustrative purposes, the animals are not to scale).

1 - Salpa
2 - Pinna nobilis
3 - Chlamis hyalina
4 - Stella chaetaster
5 - Natica stercusmuscarum
6 - Typhis sowerbyi
7 - Rissoa
8 - *Angler fish*
9 - *Sea horse*
10 - Haminoaea navicula
11 - Tricola tenuis
12 - Tricolia pullus
13 - Bittium
14 - Lima hians
15 - Hinia reticulata
16 - Venerupis senegalensis
17 - Solemya togata

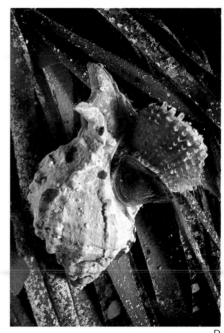

D

D - The triton Charonia lampas, a large predator common in many seas, as it devours a bivalve on a seagrass meadow of the Red Sea. This triton is not due to the movements of the adult animal, who lives its entire life in a limited area of the sea bed, but rather to the duration of its life in the planktonic larval state, when it can be carried great distances by the marine current.

C

A *The shell of this Australian trochid, Cantharidus lehmani, can be distinguished by its tall shell and beautiful axial coloration. Here it is crawling in a leaf of a marine phanerogam.*

B - *A small, graceful trochid from European seas, Calliostoma zizyphinum customarily grazes on sea bed meadows. It is most frequently seen at about 10 meters deep.*

A

lives in the Galapagos Islands and along the Pacific coast of Central America, (the Panamic malacological province). Its greenish, small, fragile, thin shell is formed of two valves, just like a clam. But what's incredible is that *Berthelina* is a true snail, a gastropod. The apex of one valve has only a hint of the spiral shape that characterizes this class of mollusks, but its body leaves no shadow of a doubt of its nomenclature: it has a foot used for crawling, a head with two pairs of tentacles, and a mouth with a radula. Essentially, the anatomy of a true snail. But this one can fully retract its body into its shell, closing

C

D

the valves hermetically like a clam.

In areas of the sea that are relatively sheltered from wave motion, on solid substrata at shallow depths, there are meadows of algae exposed directly to the sunlight *(photophilic algae)*. Mollusks take refuge from the light, so the little snails that populate the cracks in the rocks and the detritus at the foot of algae come out primarily at night and begin to creep up the thalli. If sea conditions suddenly deteriorate or if some threatening presence disturbs them, they fall onto the sea floor and head back to their shelters. In the Mediterranean, truly graceful little snails graze on the thalli of photophilic algae. For example, there is Tricolia pullus, from the Tricoliidae family. No more than 10 millimeters long, it has an extraordinary variety of patterns on the glossy surface of its shell. If you observe a collection of these little snails with a 10X lens, you'll be amazed at the pattern of spiral or radiating bands, either broken or continuous, undulating or uniform, that combine and contrast tones of red, black, white and beige. Less colorful, but with just as elegant a design, is a much larger member of the *Phasianellidae* family (which is closely related to *Tricoliidae*), from southern Australia, *Phasianella australis,* which lives in meadows of Cymodocea.

Meadows of algae and marine phanerogams are the preferred habitats of the *Rissoidae* family, which has about a hundred species in seas all over the world. They are never particularly colorful, but their sculptures are often truly elegant. Identifying a rissoid - always with the use of a good lens, or better yet, a

stereoscopic microscope, is a fascinating task, as it is to make a specialized collection of them (which has the advantage of fitting into just one drawer). A small and very graceful representative of the *Neritidae* family, *Smaragdia viridis,* with a beautiful bright green color rather rare for marine shells, frequents both algae and phanerogam meadows on all the Atlantic coasts of Europe, America and Africa. There are also mollusks that frequent meadows of photophilic algae, remaining at the base of plants without crawling over or eating them, especially during the juvenile phase. Some species that behave in this manner are a *graceful murex, Ocinebrina edwardsi,* and *Gibberula caelata,* a tiny margin shell that inhabits European seas.

Phanerogam meadows are very different from the photophilic algae environment. Phanerogams are true land plants that have conquered the marine environment. Unlike algae, they flower and bear fruit and anchor to the seabed with roots. To avoid being suffocated by the sand, marine phanerogams like Posidonia oceanica, grow vertically above the sediment

C, D - Pinna nobilis, one of the largest bivalves in existence, in the Posidonia oceanica *meadow of the Mediterranean. The byssus the mollusk uses to anchor itself to the bottom was once spun and used to make gloves and other accessories that were particularly light and prized.*

E - We usually think of a chiton as a small animal doomed to crawl along the bottom, but this elegant Ischnochiton longicymba *was instead caught by the camera as it was crawling up a leaf of a large marine phanerogam in the waters of Cape Leeuwin, Australia.*

B

E

A - *This* Norrisia norrisi, *a graceful trochid from California, feeds on sea-tangles and other algae just below the lower tidal line. The brilliant red body of the animal is quite characteristic. It is abundant in its territory, which runs from Point Conception to central Baja California.*

A

B

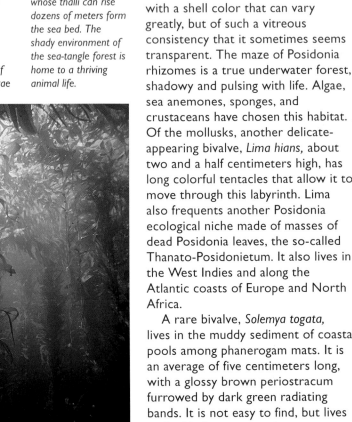

C

B - *Two graceful* Alia carinata *photographed on the thallus of an alga. These little snails from the Columbellidae family, less than 10 millimeters long, live from southern Alaska* to Baja California (Mexico), on any type of marine vegetation, from the low tide mark to about 5 meters deep. In particular, they can be found in forests of great sea-tangles, Macrocystis pyrifera.

C - *Trochids from the genus* Tegula *as they graze on the sea-tangle vegetation in California waters.*

D - *The fantastic environment of the underwater forest of sea-tangles. The algae* photographed belong to the species Macrocystis pyrifera, *whose thalli can rise dozens of meters form the sea bed. The shady environment of the sea-tangle forest is home to a thriving animal life.*

that accumulates around their rhizomes, to form characteristic table-shaped rises known as mats. This phenomenon enlivens the seabed, because channels open up among the mats where the current carries and accumulates the hulls of dead shells and other detritus. Sometimes the mats are arranged in a circle around a coastal pool, or accompany the slope of the seabed, forming steps. They thus form microhabitats that offer a large variety of conditions to hundreds of animal and plant species. Mollusks are abundant within them.

A small, elegant bivalve, *Lissopecten hyalinus,* attaches to the ribbon-like leaves of Posidonia. It is little more than two centimeters in diameter, with a shell color that can vary greatly, but of such a vitreous consistency that it sometimes seems transparent. The maze of Posidonia rhizomes is a true underwater forest, shadowy and pulsing with life. Algae, sea anemones, sponges, and crustaceans have chosen this habitat. Of the mollusks, another delicate-appearing bivalve, *Lima hians,* about two and a half centimeters high, has long colorful tentacles that allow it to move through this labyrinth. Lima also frequents another Posidonia ecological niche made of masses of dead Posidonia leaves, the so-called Thanato-Posidonietum. It also lives in the West Indies and along the Atlantic coasts of Europe and North Africa.

A rare bivalve, *Solemya togata,* lives in the muddy sediment of coastal pools among phanerogam mats. It is an average of five centimeters long, with a glossy brown periostracum furrowed by dark green radiating bands. It is not easy to find, but lives in the Mediterranean, the

D

Porscaletuguese Atlantic and as far as Senegal. The same environment is also home to a gigantic bivalve, *Pinna nobilis,* up to 90 centimeters high, which lives in the detritus of channels among the mats. In the past it was gathered for its byssus, which was used in the textile industry, and over past decades it was overharvested for food or rather tasteless souvenirs. Now it is a protected species, and should you ever run across one alive, you should simply photograph it and never tell any casual acquaintances on the beach where you found it. A snail that frequents channels among the mats is *Gyroscala lamellosa,* as elegant as its cousins the wentletraps, also members of the *Epitoniidae* family. In the same environment, but buried in the sediment, lives a clam, Venerupis senegalensis, that looks very similar to the *Tapes philippinarum* of East Asia, now cultivated in many parts of the world. On the two shores of the Atlantic, in the algae of the infralittoral band, lives the opisthobranch *Bulla striata,* which has an oval-shaped, rather light shell. The last whorl is larger than the preceding ones and completely covers the spire. Along the coast of northern Brazil, algae meadows are home to Modulus modulus, a average-sized snail with a rather robust shell and a very distinct head with two long tentacles. Surprisingly, its eyes are about halfway up the tentacles.

E

F

E, F – The forests of large seaweeds represent a rich pasture for numerous species of gastropods (E) and at the same time offer them excellent places to hide from predators.

THE MANGROVE FORESTS

Mangroves mark the border between the marine world and dry land along many tropical coasts less exposed to the surf. Vegetation takes hold along the sandy and muddy beaches of lagoons, at river mouths, in sheltered bays, and on the leeward side of islands. These are extraordinarily productive environments in biological terms: they are home to a myriad of fish, birds, crustaceans and mollusks, who find both food and shelter within them. Mangrove forests are not, however, an ideal coastal environment for mass tourism, which prefers sandy beaches or reefs, coral or otherwise, and always demands clear water. Thus, in coastal areas that have recently been developed and urbanized, mangrove forests are unfortunately destroyed to make room not only for ports and industrial development, but also for swimming beaches and traditional seaside promenades.

In mangrove forests, the trees have adapted to setting their roots in an asphyxiated soil drenched with salty or brackish water. To survive, they have devised ingenious systems - they expel the salt from their tissues using something like pores, which deposit it on the bark, and propagate not by seeds, but through little fully-developed plants that float on the water until the tide leaves them in a place where they

A, C - In the mangrove forest in the Caribbean, cluster of oysters (Dendrostrea frons) form around the trunks and roots of plants. Many oysters (A) in the vegetation of Sanibel, Florida, during low tide in the midlittoral band. In C, a detail. No more than 7 centimeters long, with an often irregular form, this oyster has the peculiarity of producing groups of tiny pearls along the edge of the shell. It is common from Florida to Brazil.

Drawing B – In this illustration we can see the population of molluscs in a mangrove forest in Florida, in the Caribbean province. For illustrative purposes, the mollusks are not shown in correct proportion to the vegetation or each other.

1 - Littorina scabra
2 - Neritina virginia
3 - Isognomon alatus
4 - Cypraea zebra
5 - Phacoides pectinatus
6 - Batillaria minima
7 - Melongena corona

C

105

can take root. They breathe oxygen directly from the air, using special aerial branches called pneumotophores, and they develop a system for anchoring to unstable ground so they can withstand the flow of the tides.

It only easy to visit the edge of this extremely interesting natural environment, or degraded areas where the vegetation is sparse. By boat, you can easily traverse the part of the forest facing the sea, but entering it is a very difficult enterprise. The maze of aerial roots and branches is extremely dense, while the sandy or detrital soil, especially where fresh water enters from rivers and streams, quickly develops a layer of black, slimy mud that is absolutely impassable. And collecting shells? In an environment like this, it's better to give up the do-it-yourself attitude and let local fishermen give you a hand. Only about a hundred species of mollusks throughout the world have chosen mangrove forests as their habitat. The supralittoral band, which is here represented by mangrove trunks, branches and leaves, is inhabited by species of pulmonates and prosobranchs

A

B

that seem to be evolving more towards a terrestrial existence than a marine one. Thus, in Australian mangroves (which line the whole north coast of the continent, from Queensland to Northwest Australia), *Littorina filosa,* like various species of the genus from the rocky coasts of temperate zones, spends much of its existence out of the water. The females of this slender snail, about 25 millimeters long with a shell that varies from yellow to red to brown, enter the water only after mating, to lay their eggs. After a brief period in the water, young hatchlings settle on tree branches, from which the males never descend. This choice of aerial lifestyle has led to a transformation of the mantle cavity into a organ that acts as a lung.

On the other hand, the ellobiids are true pulmonates, and there are various species of them in the mangrove forests of Australia. The one with the most noticeable shell in form and size is *Ellobium aurismidae,* whose white shell covered with a blackish *periostracum* can reach a length of 76 millimeters. The shell of *Ellobium aurisjudae,* which has a chestnut-colored periostracum, is whitish with a more slender form, and is no more than 50 millimeters long. The small Pythia scarabaeus, no more than 25 millimeters long, is perfectly adapted to dry substrata, and lays its eggs on leaves that are not dampened by the tide, while *Cassidula rugata,* even smaller, frequents the upper band of the midlittoral band, thus living both an aerial and an aquatic life on a daily basis. All *ellobiids,* who have no operculum, have developed teeth around the aperture of the shell that prevent predators from entering.

While *ellobiids* are a family of substantially terrestrial mollusks who still long for the marine environment, the potamidids are a clearly marine family, with a shell form and anatomy very similar to the cerithids. They live in estuary environments (hence the name, from the Greek potamos, or river) and are well represented in mangrove forests. They are all herbivores and feed on tiny algae. In Australia, the large *Pyrazus ebeninus* is quite common and exceeds 10 centimeters in length. The aborigines used it for food, and the English navigator James Cook, who discovered the continent, found enormous quantities in Botany Bay, where the Gulf of Sydney is today.

Widespread in mangroves throughout much of the Indopacific area, from China to Madagascar, is *Telescopium telescopium,* with its beautiful conical-shaped shell,

C

A - A cluster of oysters from the species Crassotrea virginica *has formed around the aerial root of a* Rhizophora.

B - *A population of* Terebralia palustris *scattered over a "field" of pneumatophores on the mud of a mangrove formation in Oman.*

C - *The mangrove forests of St. George Basin, Kimberley, Australia, feed vast populations of mollusks who have adapted to the environment. The mangrove mollusks from the family of* Ellobiidae, *live on trunks or leaves of mangroves and have adopted aerial respiration.*

blackish with very thin light stripes, 9 centimeters high. In the same area lives *Cerithidea cingulata,* up to 50 millimeters high, with its elegant shell adorned by a network of axial and spiral stripes, with three little bands of beading in different colors for each whorl. Billions of shells of this and related species can be found in every square kilometer in the mangroves of the Philippines.

One potamidid from the West African province, *Tympanotonus fuscatus,* is quite variable in form, with a shell that is sometimes almost smooth and sometimes adorned by a regular band of spines; it lives in the muddy sand of the mangroves, in the midlittoral band, and feeds on the organic surface pellicle

A nerite from the mangroves of the West Central Pacific, *Neritina communis,* is extremely abundant, with shells in elegant designs and colors. It is about 20 millimeters in diameter and is adorned by pink, red, yellow, white and black bands in primarily zigzag patterns. It's easy to find in souvenir shops. The dark-colored *Nerita lineata,* relatively large for the nerite family, lives in the midlittoral band. It is no larger than 38 millimeters, and many of its shells are inhabited by hermit crabs. *Nassarius olivaceus,* with a brown shell about 25 millimeters long, is a necrophage, and can occasionally be found alive within rotting trunks. A melongenid, *Melongena corona* (locally known as king's crown or crown conch), with an extremely variable but quite beautiful shell, lives in the mangroves of Florida, Alabama and the Yucatan peninsula. It may vary greatly in size, and adult specimens range from only two and a half centimeters to over 20 centimeters long! Its ornamentation may also vary greatly. The crown that gives the species its name may be formed by a single row of spines with a triangular cross section, or by two rows, or may

even be absent. In addition to dwarf and giant specimens, some of them are very tapered, others stubby. In the past, races and subspecies were created that proved to have little taxonomic value, while they are sought by collectors. *Melongena corona* lives in the shade of the mangroves, where it feeds primarily on dead fish, crustaceans and mollusks, but it does not hesitate to attack living mollusks, like gastropods from the genus *Fasciolaria* and bivalves, in particular oysters.

Among the bivalves, an oyster that has colonized the mangroves, but has adapted to other situations as well, and is in fact subject to intensive cultivation, is *Saccostrea commercialis,* which, as the scientific name indicates, is quite popular in fish markets. A lucinid, *Anodontia edentula,* lives in the waters at the edge of mangroves in the Indopacific region, deeply embedded in the mud. It is 35 millimeters in diameter, with massive,

swollen, white, perfectly circular valves. A frequent bivalve in mangroves in the Caribbean, from Florida to Brazil, is the isognomid *Isognomon alatus:* its valves are not hinged by teeth but by a very long, thick ligament, the resilium, which has parallel segments perpendicular to the edge of the valves, a characteristic common to the entire family.

But the largest bivalve that colonizes the mud of mangrove seabeds is a gigantic teredinid from the genus Kufus, which reaches a length of about ninety centimeters. It lives in the South Western Pacific. It digs a tunnel with two small valves and transforms it into a very long calcareous tube. Only the tips of the siphons poke out of the mud, and the creature uses them to circulate the water of the seabed through its organic filters, to remove suspended nourishment and oxygen: local populations gather Kufus for food.

A

FROM THE HIGH SEA

Once it has decided to leave the seabed and wander freely through the immense oceans, what can a mollusk do with a shell it inherited from ancestors that crept lazily over just a few meters? Wouldn't that shield made to protect the exposed side of the body stretched out on a hard surface, prove to be perfectly useless in a three dimensional space, where predators can attack in a flash from any direction? In effect, the solution of

C

getting rid of the shell, which does seem logical according to human experience - swimming with a backpack on your shoulders is possible, but it's easier without it - was the choice of many mollusks that became pelagic, i.e. who left the resources of the marine seabed to seek nourishment in the open water. This is what the octopus did. This is what the nudibranchs did, with their beautiful forms and colors that have given them the name of sea butterflies. But there have been many interesting exceptions. In many cases, the question, What do we do with the shell? has led to unpredictable evolutionary responses. There was even a genus of pelagic mollusks who discarded their original shell and then invented a completely new one to protect their young. It is known as the argonaut (Argonauta), a cephalopod who is a distant relative of the octopus. The female, who is a giant compared to the male, builds an ootheca, an egg case, in the form of a little boat, where it lays and keeps its eggs as it swims in the high sea. Sometimes the current pushes it toward the coast and the poor argonaut ends up on the beach.

The purple snail (Janthina) is a true snail with a very light, but classically formed shell. It travels under the surface of the sea attached to a raft it makes by sticking together bubbles of mucus filled with air. To make the bubbles, it stretches out part of its foot from the water. Some species of purple snail (including Janthina nitens from European seas) also attach their egg capsules to this raft. They are

prolific mothers, and can lay as many as two million eggs each, arranged in about 500 capsules. The purple snail is carnivorous and easily devours colonies of polyps of the Portuguese man-of-war (Physalia) and the tissues of jellyfish and other planktonic coelenterates, despite the fact that they are protected by stinging cells capable of killing much larger animals than it. You need to be very lucky to find intact purple snail shells on the beach. On rare occasions, the sea will toss up large quantities, but years may go by before even one arrives along a stretch of coast. There are descriptions of about thirty species of purple snail. It can be found in seas throughout the world, except for polar regions. Its mimetic colors run from pale blue to purple. If it feels threatened, the purple snail emits a substance that tinges the water violet, thus confusing its predator.

Another planktonic gastropod, the Peron's sea butterfly (Atlanta peronii), has an extremely small, fragile,

B - A swimming argonaut. The ancients imagined that the mollusk used its pseudo-shell, which we know is an ootheca, or egg case, to float as if on a true boat. Although the female argonaut (the photo shows an Argonauta argus) is the only one who builds an ootheca, caring for young is a common trait in cephalopods, who to some extent look after their eggs until they hatch.

C - This Indopacific cuttlefish, Metasepia pfefferi, can be distinguished by its bright colors.

D - This small octopus, Hapalochlaena maculosa, has the most powerful poison of any related species. It lives in southern Australia.

D

transparent shell. It can swim actively, as it has transformed the front part of its foot, known as the *propodium*, into a sort of fin. This allows it to venture into deep waters, and it has been found as deep as 3000 meters below the surface (on the other hand, if the purple snail loses contact with its raft, it sinks and dies). The central part of the sea butterfly's foot, the *mesopodium*, instead has a sucker that the animal uses to stick to its prey, which it devours by lacerating its tissues with a radula. The *cavolinia* (*Cavolinia*, an opisthobranch) has pelagic habits and similar swimming abilities, but it uses two lobes of the foot as fins, which have developed outward and laterally. Its small, fragile shell has a globular form quite different from that of snails.

Unlike the argonaut, some cephalopods produce true shells. These include the internal shell produced by the cuttlefish (*Sepia*) and

the squid *(Loligo)*, in common parlance known as cuttlebone and pen; the former is calcareous and the latter horny. If all shells were so unattractive, certainly no one would collect them, but they're a necessary part of any naturalistic collection.

A true jewel, and strong point of any collection, is the shell of the nautilus (*Nautilus*), which lives in the Indopacific. This is a true living fossil that has remained practically unchanged for 500 million years. In this case as well, as in fossil ammonites, the spiral is coiled around a single plane, but the last whorl of the shell coils around the earlier ones and hides them, creating a globular form of rare elegance. It is no wonder that the shell of the nautilus has always been used by sculptors and goldsmiths. The interior of the shell is made up of little chambers that the animal abandons as it grows,

A

B

closing them off by a calcareous diaphragm in the center of which it leaves a little hole. A siphon runs through the series of little holes and allows the mollusk to pump gas into the interior of the shell, thus changing its specific weight and allowing it to move vertically. In other words, it has a mechanism similar to a fish's air bladder or the immersion chamber of a submarine. For horizontal movement, the nautilus uses the principle of a reaction engine,

forcefully expelling water through contractions of its mantle, much as octopuses, cuttlefish and squid do. But while these distant relatives have a maximum of about ten tentacles, the nautilus has an impressive quantity of from 60 to 90, but with no suckers. It has four gills, no ink sac, and very primitive eyes. There are three species of nautilus in the warm waters of the Southwest Pacific. Fishermen catch it in nets at depths of between fifty and a hundred

meters, where it wanders in search of its preferred prey, lobsters and shrimp.

The shell of another cephalopod, the spirula (Spirula), has a structure and functions similar to the nautilus, but is much more modest in size and appearance. It is coiled in a flat spiral, but its indentations are disjointed, and most of the spiral is covered by the mollusk's body. The spirula is usually found at between 50 and 500 meters in depth. It is not an impressive addition to a collection, but it is still a naturalistic curiosity.

There are relatively few pelagic species of mollusks, and the overwhelming majority of species in the *phylum* are part of the benthos and live on seabeds. At least this is true of adult life.

During larval existence, most marine mollusks are part of the plankton, and sea currents are used to disperse their multitudinous young.

A - With its foot transformed into a swimming organ and its sturdy yet extremely light shell, this Hydatina hydatis *snail leads an entirely pelagic life.*

B - A rare case of a pelagic prosobranch, a Janthina janthina *is feeding on the tentacle of a coelenterate, the*

Portuguese man-of-war, *whose scientific name is* Physalia utriculus. *Small cirripeds have settled on the outside of the shell.*

Collecting a shell during a walk along the beach or a dive over a beautiful seabed is an instinctive gesture, as is buying a beautiful one that somehow beckons you from a sales stand in the tropics. For some, the young or the young at heart, the attraction to shells and the worlds they evoke leads them to start a collection. Usually the first shells found, bought or received as gifts end up in a glass jar or lined up on a shelf as a reminder of a wonderful

Images from the whole chapter - There are different criteria that can be used to arrange shell collections. According to a tradition that dates back to the ìWunderkammerî of cultured persons of the 18th century, the collection is displayed using essentially aesthetic criteria, placing the strangest and most surprising forms in a showcase or in drawers with compartments separated by a sheet of glass. For study purposes, however, after selecting and identifying the materials, it is better to arrange them according to a zoological criterion, i.e. using the classification indicated in manuals, which takes account of the kinship between families of mollusks

based on their descent from common ancestors. Today, as computers become common in private homes, it is certainly appropriate to arrange all significant data on the collection in a good database (thus saving yourself the work of preparing charts, registers and index cards by hand) and identifying the discovery with just a number. You can thus let the database systematically order the collection, while the shells can be placed in plastic sacks and boxes to protect them from dust, and arranged as you like, according to aesthetic criteria or in a way that saves space. Nevertheless, donít forget that shells prefer the dark; exposure to light will fade their colors.

vacation, an exciting dive, perhaps a happy love affair, but when you make the decision to obtain others, and perhaps also a book to help you identify them and tell you more about them, a collection project begins to take shape. At this point, it's best to be sure that your collection will be a success and give you all the satisfaction that a naturalistic collection can provide.

Of course, any plans to make a collection are based on more or less conscious motivations. With regard to shells, one thing should be cleared up immediately: if you want to obtain costly specimens as well, you should know that they are never a good investment of your money. It's true that there are pieces than can cost a very great deal due to their rarity and beauty. But, as experience of the past two centuries has shown, even the rarest and most beautiful shells, whose few known specimens were found only by chance, usually in the stomachs of fish, sooner or later became cheap when fishermen discovered their habitat and sold them in large quantities. A shell collection is very satisfying in terms of beauty and knowledge, calms the soul and takes you to marvelous worlds...but it will never make you rich.

A passion for shells takes a leap in quality when the pleasure of collecting them goes from being aesthetic to naturalistic, and possession of specimens is no longer the only purpose, but becomes a tool for learning more about the sea and its creatures, about what happens in an underwater cave, or a forest of oarweed, and how the animal that made those fascinating shells actually functions. The following suggestions are for naturalistic collectors, and are based on the practice of generations of shell enthusiasts.

You should make one decision as soon as you can: what kind of

collection do you want? Specialized by family, environment, or geographical area? Needless to say, trying to make a complete or nearly complete collection of all marine shells is impossibility dream - not even the most splendid museums in the world have them. When making this decision, it's a good idea to think about where you live and your lifestyle. If you have a house near the sea or regularly frequent a stretch of coast or an island, you might aim for a local collection. Done well, it could even become scientifically important, not necessarily due to the discovery of new species, but certainly in deepening knowledge of the environment. Anyone who enjoys spending time at the stereoscopic microscope could aim for a collection of micromollusks: you can obtain bags of detritus collected from seabeds that are true treasure troves of specimens. One advantage of a collection of micromollusks is that the whole collection can fit into a drawer or little more. You can devote your collection to just one family: those with beautiful shells are obviously preferable. The most popular shells for collection in the world are cowries, followed by cones. Only someone who has truly enormous financial resources and the time for international shopping can collect a rare, beautiful and costly family of shells like the pleurotomarids.

Shells can be contemplated for their many aesthetic values. But to enter the enchanted world of these sea treasures, it's not enough to contemplate them. You need to read them, understand them, recognize them. It's an exercise with various levels of difficulty. It's almost always easy to read adult shells in excellent condition that are at least one centimeter in size, which are usually found in price lists in the collectors market or in stands at fish markets. But you should practice distinguishing the details of even easy shells, for example, comparing the murices sold in fish markets with those found on the beach. You also need to know how to recognize immature shells and classify them under the right species. Often juvenile forms are very unlike the adult form, and it's easy to classify children as a different species from their parents (an error that even reputable malacologists have committed!). Obtaining examples of intermediate phases by collecting shells of increasing size from detritus and trying to arrange them in order of growth will help you avoid mistakes of this kind. It's also helpful to practice on washed up shells that have been calcined by the sun and polished by the beach. When many important details have been eliminated, it's not always easy to identify the shell. Day after day, as you examine large quantities of materials, you'll develop the diagnostic eye you need to write up an index card (or create a computer file) on the shell, with information on where you found it and a naturalistic observation of the seabed visited. For beginner enthusiasts, an important goal is being able to classify the shell by family. From here, consulting malacological atlases by geographical area, or collections of specialized periodicals in the library, you will be able to identify even less common species (the index published in the final part of this volume is organized so you can identify families, as well as the individual species illustrated).

Is an intact specimen of an adult shell proving hard to identify? That is, is properly reading its characteristics (size, form, ornamentation, color, and glossiness) not enough to classify the species? It could happen. Sometimes even commonplace shells, even the clams sold in fish markets, may have shells with characteristics somewhere between the typical features of two very similar species, and this often generates interesting discussions in meetings of shell enthusiasts. In cases like this, what should you do? If it is only a question of writing up an index card to place the shell in your collection, don't worry, just note your doubts in anticipation of learning more in the future, knowing that a

specimen that may seem doubtful is certainly no less interesting than others. For example, you could note the following for a true clam with a shell that could be either a cultivated Indopacific area species (the Japanese littleneck), always called a true clam in restaurants, or a European clam fished in the open water: Tapes cf. decussatus (Linneaus 1758), cf. philippinarum (Adams & Reeve, 1850) (cf. is an abbreviation that means compare). Naturally, as better informed connoisseurs know, there are no doubts if you have the whole animal before you instead of a shell: the Indopacific clam has horns (more properly called siphons) that are welded together, while the European clam's siphons are detached.

In truly doubtful cases, an examination of the soft parts is actually the only way to identify a find (i.e. place it under an already

described species) and classify it (i.e. give it a taxonomic position and a name, if it is unknown to science). Today, professional malacologists use sophisticated microscopes to examine the details of the radula or genital apparatus, and also use statistical methods to study diagnostic aspects for entire populations of mollusks. This rigor is gradually giving some order to mollusk nomenclature. In the past, when an examination of only shell characteristics was deemed sufficient to create a new species, many authors published their discoveries as species new to science, when they were in reality only manifestations of normal individual variability or at the most distinctive features of a race or subspecies. This created a great deal of confusion and a mass of synonyms in successive publications.

In any event, until an enthusiast

decides to become a researcher he does not need to use a microscope to examine the organs of mollusks to identify his finds. This is in part due to the fortunate fact that there are few cases where shell features cannot be read, and these ate micromollusks, especially ground and fresh water species and deep marine species, which have small, unattractive shells that are not desirable in anything but the most specialized collections.

THE INFORMATION TO KEEP.
The first step in starting a good collection is to record all important information about how you found (or acquired) each specimen or lot. Until recently, we would have suggested writing everything on a card in pen, but today it's faster and better to enter everything in your home computer data bank. The box on this page gives you an outline for a typical registration, based on that used for the mollusk census for the coasts of Italy that the Italian Malacological Society performed in collaboration with ENEA (National Agency for Energy and the Environment). It makes no difference if many cards have empty boxes, but it is important for the data to be accurate. In the beginning, it's not even necessary to determine the name of the species. Even in scientific research, this information may be left hanging for years, although a beginner tends to believe it is more important than anything else. If you can't answer the question, What shell is this? write cf. (i.e. compare) followed by the name of a species that seems similar, and go on. It's better to leave an empty space than make an identification you're not sure of. Accurate notes are potentially very useful. Don't forget that many people who began gathering shells for personal pleasure later became full-time scientists, going from shell enthusiasts to malacologists, discovering new species and writing fine pages in the great book of natural science. Even if you have no such ambitions in the beginning, you should start off right. For this reason, when you acquire shells, either as a gift or through exchanges, you should insist on obtaining as much information as possible (including the original files, if they exist). This second or third hand information should nevertheless be treated with much caution. When in doubt, better to leave a blank space than write something wrong. The safest shells are those you personally collect or receive from experts associated with malacological circles, then come those acquired from specialized merchants who distribute detailed price lists. With rare exceptions, souvenir dealers know nothing about shells and do not even know what a collector needs.

THE SEARCH FOR SHELLS.
An old rule says that shells are where you happen to find them, and in fact luck plays a very important role. But some basic knowledge of marine environments like that presented in this book, is always helpful.

It may seem unnecessary, but experience has proved that we need to insist on one thing: be careful as you search, so you don't endanger either yourself or your companions. Exploring an environment requires a great deal of time and should be considered a job rather than a pleasure swim. While you explore environments and gather your finds, the tide rises or falls, and the currents, waves and wind could change direction or intensity. When you're underwater searching the seabed, the air in your tank always seems to finish faster than you had expected, especially if you are exerting effort like turning over rocks and scraping walls, and if you emerge far from the boat or the shore, you may be exhausted your strength. Thus, even in situations that seem easy, work times and movements should be planned and followed, and you should stay well within the equipment tables and your own energy reserves. In the sea, you should always expect the unexpected.

A NOTE ABOUT CLOTHING AND EQUIPMENT.

There are still people who venture onto reefs barefoot and on coral formations wearing only swimming trunks. Don't follow their example when you go looking for shells. An emerged reef should only be explored when the sea is calm, wearing sturdy closed sandals with anti-slip soles, and protecting your head and body from the sun, perhaps wearing a pair of pajamas. To keep your hands free, you should tie a plastic bag around your belt for finds which require no special protection, while delicate shells should be carried in a plastic container with a large mouth and screw top. A pair of very thin steel tweezers is indispensable for collecting small specimens in the fissures of rocks.

When you explore a tidal or underwater area, you need to add a mask and mouthpiece, thin gloves that your hands can feel through, and a scuba knife. Water temperature may be dangerous. If you're in temperate waters in summer and early autumn, you'll need an average thickness wetsuit, about 5 millimeters of neoprene, while in other seasons or when the water is cold, you'll need a thicker, or dry wetsuit. If you plan to collect micromollusks that may be found on rocks encrusted with calcareous algae, anellids, and bryozoans, you'll need to scrape samples of the surface and collect all the material, which you can examine later at your leisure. You can use a garden trowel with a very short handle, and a steel net with a handle where you can gather the material removed from the wall.

On tropical coral reefs, you need to wear padded boots as well as a mask, thin gloves, a mouthpiece and flippers, and don't forget a very light wetsuit (or if you don't have one, normal pajamas will do), whatever the temperature of the water is. Clearly, this equipment would be too much for a swimmer, but a shell enthusiast is there to work, and you need to arm yourself against fire coral stings, cuts caused by accidental contact with razor-sharp corals, and the sun, which mercilessly punishes the ignorant and careless.

CLEANING AND CONSERVING THE MATERIAL COLLECTED.

The sea is fragrant, but after only a short time everything that comes out of it smells bad. Ideally, all shells collected should be cleaned within 24 hours. If you can't, as is usually the case when you're travelling, the fastest system is to store everything in salt, or even a mixture of 50 percent water and alcohol, in hermetically sealed containers, of course. This method has the drawback of causing the tissues of the mollusks gathered to harden somewhat, which may complicate later cleaning of gastropods with a spiral shell, but it is only a minor problem compared with allowing a bad smell to ruin the pleasure of your trip.

There are differing views on the best method of cleaning your shells. Once it was advised to quickly boil everything collected, but now many believe that boiling can ruin the color and may even crack more fragile shells. If you have a freezer, you can freeze mollusks, and after one or two days bring them back to room temperature and eliminate the soft parts. For bivalves, just cut the adductor muscles from their housing, being careful not to break the hinge. By gently heating it, you can close the valves together until they meet perfectly, and you can tie the shell in a closed position with sewing thread. After a couple of days or less, you can cut the thread, and the hinge, now dry, will no longer open the valves. If in the future you need to reopen the shell to examine the inside, just briefly heat the hinge,

which will become elastic again, and you can repeat the operation when you put the specimen back in the collection. If, despite all precautions, the ligament breaks, or if you want to put back together a shell you have found with its valves separated, just use a bit of flour and water paste on the hinge to put the specimen back together again. It's not a good idea to use a commercial glue, because if you need to separate the valves in the future, the flour paste, unlike the glue, can easily be dissolved with a bit of water.

It's a bit more difficult to remove the soft parts from spiral gastropods. You'll need some patience at first, and experience will do the rest. Using a pair of tweezers, firmly grasp the soft parts and try to remove them from the shell without breaking them. By pulling gently but continuously, without jerking, you'll usually succeed, especially when the animal's tissues are still intact. If, despite your efforts, fragments of the intestinal tract remain in the bottom of the shell, use a piece of wire to make a spiral that ends in a hook. Working delicately, you'll be able to extract the fragments. It may also help to put the shell under running water. When you're sure that the shell is completely empty inside, it's a good idea to immerse it briefly in a weak bleach solution, which will clean and deodorize it, and then let it dry in the shade on a shelf for several days. Finally, if you note that despite everything, the shell still smells bad, you should drip candle wax inside it and then stop the opening with a cotton ball soaked in perfume. When you prepare a gastropod with an operculum, you should always take this out when you remove the soft parts, allow it to dry along with the shell, and then place it in its natural position before the opening, using a drop of glue to affix it to a cotton ball.

Everything becomes much more simple when you are preparing micromollusks, which are never more than five or six millimeters in size. After keeping them in alcohol for a few days, just leave them in the open in the shade to allow the soft parts to dry out without leaving any bad odor. Preparation of chitons requires a bit more care, because these little animals tend to roll up into a ball, making it impossible to distend them without breaking them. Right after you catch them, you need to immobilize them by tying them to a small piece of wood with a bit of thread, before putting them in the freezer. Then you can prepare them or allow them to dry in the open, especially if they are very small, or else remove the soft parts, being careful not to break the girdle or disjoint the eight plates. If you want to highlight the plates to compare and study them, you must very delicately separate them from each other. They should then be glued to a piece of cardboard in the sequence they had on the living animal.

Finally, an expert collector will need to keep the soft parts of a few specimens collected for purposes of anatomical examinations, which are sometimes necessary to determine a species accurately, and are indispensable when you need to classify what you believe to be a species new to science. In this case, you should keep the specimen in a sealed container in a 30 percent alcohol solution for the first three days, which you can then replace with a 50 percent solution for the next three days, and finally a 70 percent solution for permanent storage.

During cleaning, many collectors are tempted to improve the shell's appearance by removing the periostracum, and try to eliminate any limestone encrustation with a steel pin, or by running it through a diluted acid solution. Souvenir sellers even change the shell's appearance by filing or glazing it. A serious collector would never do this, but even small things like removing the periostracum and encrustations should only be done in moderation. You should keep at least one specimen intact as it was found in nature. And remember that while acid will corrode the encrustation, it will also corrode the shell, which is made of calcium carbonate. If you must use this method to improve a specimen's appearance, the parts you want to preserve, in particular the shell's aperture, should be protected from the acid bath by dripping wax or liquid paraffin over them.

In any case, before adding a shell to your collection, it's a good idea to gently rub it with vaseline oil (the baby oil you can find in your drugstore), and then dry it. This treatment will improve the beauty of your find by bringing out its colors, and will protect it over time.

Shells are beautiful to look at, and a collector rightly likes to display at least the most showy or prized pieces. There's one problem. Light and dust deteriorate the surface of the shell, which over time will appear calcined, just like shells that have lain in the sunlight on the beach. If you really want to display some specimens, it's best to do it in a display case with smoked glass, out of direct sunlight.

The best way to conserve shells is to keep them in a chest of low drawers, placing each specimen,

EXAMPLE OF RECORD TO ENTER IN DATA BASE
(the "fields" in bold type, the information to be added as a record in regular type):

SERIAL NUMBER: given to each individual specimen or lot of specimens of the same species and origin as they enter the collection.

DATE OF RECORDING: the date the specimen entered the collection; should be typed in to permit numerical operations

FAMILY: the scientific name, if necessary indicating any common synonym between parentheses.

SPECIES: genus, species, author, date of publication, entered according to the conventions of naturalistic literature.

PLACEMENT: the section of the collection in which it is kept; if the collection is strictly systematic, this can be omitted.

SPECIMENS: if it is a lot with more than one item.

IDENTIFIED BY: the name of the person or institution that made the identification..

PURCHASED: where, when, from whom, price.

GIVEN: by whom, when.

FOUND BY: name of the collector

LOCATION: as precise as possible an indication of the place found.

DATE: (the date found.

TIDE: high, medium, low.

COLLECTION METHOD: by hand from the shore, by hand while diving, with nets or dredges if caught by fishing boats)

DISTANCE FROM THE SHORE in meters.

AT DEPTH (in meters).

TYPE OF SEABED (rocky, shingly-pebbly, sandy, muddy, coarse detritus without mud, deep detritus with very fine sand and mud, coral.

ENVIRONMENT: supralittoral, midlittoral, infralittoral, circumlittoral, lagoon, on algae, on Posidonia.

ALIVE: (yes, no.

NOTES: (other useful information regarding ecology, behavior, relative abundance or scarcity in the area, etc.) bibliographical references (publications used to identify the species or useful for other information about it)

---

along with a label containing the essential data, within a little transparent plastic box. Specialized stores sell all sizes. For micromollusks, the most practical boxes are square, about two centimeters wide and one centimeter high. Very fragile specimens can be held between the box cover and a cotton ball in contrasting color, which will bring out the details of the shell.

In this way, the collection will be easily accessible, but at the same time well protected from accidental blows to the chest and other mishaps. The order in which you place the boxes is a personal choice. If you have enough room, it's better to follow systematic order, as museum collections do. In any event, it's practical to keep very large specimens in a special chest with large drawers..

Finally, you need to consider your study equipment. A pair of good magnifying lenses is indispensable, a 5X for your first examination of the shell's details, and a 10X (counting glass) lens to examine the smaller parts. If you want to collect micromollusks, you'll need at least a 20X stereoscopic microscope. You'll want steel tweezers to handle very small specimens, a little paint brush that you can moisten to handle very delicate parts, a gauge to take precise measurements, boxes, test tubes, little plastic bags and adhesive labels to keep your material in order. That's more or less all you'll need, plus a good register to note down information, or better yet, a personal computer with a good data base program.

WRITING SHELL NAMES
According to the conventions of natural science books, genus names are indicated in italics, with the first letter capitalized (for example, Cypraea) and the name of the species and any subspecies are indicated in italics with a small first letter (for example, tigris). The scientific names of the families are anglicized, with the first letter capitalized (for example, Cypreidae), while common names always appear with a small first letter (cowries). Species with a universally known name are indicated in English (mussel for Mytilus galloprovincialis) or by the anglicized scientific name (tiger cowry for Cypraea tigris) when they are commonly known among shell enthusiasts, following the usage of popular publications in the major European languages. The scientific name in Latin is always indicated when the text requires it to be intelligible.

THE SHELLS OF THE SEA

Stenoplax conspicua
Ischnochitonidae

Lives in America along the Pacific coast, from Santa Barbara to the Gulf of California, under rocks in the intertidal area. From 5 to 12 centimeters in size. Has a distinctive elongated form and numerous small spines on the girdle.

Tonicia elegans
Chitonidae

This graceful polyplacophore from the North American Pacific coast feeds on the pellicle of algae that forms on rocks. Less than 3.5 centimeters in length. The first chitons appeared on the Earth about 570 million years ago.

Chiton olivaceus - Green chiton
Chitonidae

The greenish color and fan-like ornamentation on the sides of the plates make it easy to identify this polyplacophore that lives on Mediterranean reefs. It feeds on algae and reaches 4 centimeters in length.

Cryptolax larvaeformis
Acanthochitonidae

Unlike other chitons, Cryptolax has only five imbricate valves, while the other three are separate. Average in size, lives the Indopacific region in the infralittoral band.

Cryptochiton stelleri
Acanthochitonidae

This is the largest chiton in the world, reaching 33 centimeters in length. It lives up to 18 meters deep, from Alaska to California. To prevent other animals from settling on its plates, it secretes a mucus that expands upon contact with water.

Pleurotomaria hirasei
Pleurotomariidae

This is the most well-known and common of this family of shells, highly prized by collectors. It is 7 to 12 centimeters in diameter and lives at depths of about 90 meters in the sea off the island of Honshu, Japan.

Pleurotomaria africana
Pleurotomariidae

This large, rare shell is found only along the South African coast, where it lives on the soft floors of the deep sea. The gradual closing of the slit on the last whorl leaves a band that traverses all whorls.

Pleurotomaria adansoniana
Pleurotomariidae

▶

Quite rare, it lives in the Caribbean along steep underwater slopes from 60 to 450 meters deep. The characteristic slit crosses about half of the shell's last whorl, which has a diameter of 15 centimeters. Sometimes it is caught in fish traps.

Haliotis tuberculata lamellosa
Abalone or lamellated haliotis
Haliotidae

This is the Mediterranean subspecies of the Atlantic Haliotis tuberculata that lives from Portugal to the Canary Islands. It is distinguished by its smaller average size (5 centimeters) and more evident lamellae. It lives on reefs in the midlittoral and infralittoral bands.

◀ **Haliotis rufescens**
Haliotidae

The largest of the abalones, it reaches 30 centimeters in length. The shell is bulky, reddish on the outside, with a pearly interior with green to pink glints. It lives from Oregon to Baja California. Its flesh is quite tasty.

▶

◀ **Haliotis asinina**
Haliotidae

This abalone, common in the Indian Ocean and Pacific, owes its name to the unusually elongated form of the shell, which is robust but light, measuring up to 10 centimeters in length.

Diodora graeca - Greek keyhole limpet
Fissurellidae

▶

Can be distinguished from others in its genus because it has few radial ribs. About 2.5 centimeters in length, it lives from the upper midlittoral to the infralittoral band, on rocky substrata, from the Mediterranean to the coast of England. Rather common.

◀ **Lottia gigantea**
Patelloidae

Lives on the rocky coasts of the Pacific, including above the high tide level, from the Canadian border to Baja California. The interior of the shell is blue-white with a brown spot. It reaches 11 centimeters in diameter.

Acmaea saccharina
Patelloidae

▶

Has a depressed profile and more or less stellate margin. Up to 4 centimeters in diameter. It is quite common along the rocky coasts of the Indian Ocean and the western Pacific, to western Australia.

Patella coerulea - Common limpet
Patellidae

Mediterranean and Portuguese species, often quite abundant in the midlittoral band of reefs. Its form and color vary widely. It is 4 to 7 centimeters in length. The interior is shiny gray with bluish glints.

Patella longicosta
Patellidae

Has a characteristic stellate form and may be up to 8 centimeters in diameter. Lives along the rocky coast of South Africa, where it is quite common. Calcareous encrustations often hide the dorsal sculpture, giving it a grayish appearance.

Patella ferruginea - Giant limpet
Patellidae

The solid, rust-colored ribs make it unmistakable. Lives in western North Africa to the Tyrrhenian coasts, where it has become quite rare due to overharvesting. Reaches 8 centimeters in diameter.

Cellana radians
Patellidae

Lives in New Zealand and is the most common of the twenty limpet species in the archipelago. It is 5 centimeters in diameter, with an extremely fine concentric sculpture and beautiful color, pink outside with glints of mother-of-pearl within.

Cellana exarata
Patellidae

Lives in Hawaii and can be distinguished by its elegant ray-shaped design formed by black ribs spotted with gray alternating with whitish furrows. It can reach 3 centimeters in height and a maximum of 8 centimeters in length.

Umbonium giganteum
Trochidae

This trochid with a lenticular, biconvex, button-shaped shell characteristic of the genus, prefers muddy floors of sheltered inlets. Reaches 4.5 centimeters in diameter. Lives in Japan.

Trochus niloticus
Trochidae

This massive trochid from the Indopacific (it can reach 12 centimeters in height in six years) has for many years been raised for its mother-of-pearl. Its natural environment is the surf area of coral reefs.

Tegula regina
Trochidae
►

It has beautiful ornamentation with radial, grayish-purple ribs with a golden yellow umbilical region. It lives in California from 5 to 25 meters in depth. Not common. An average of 4 centimeters in height.

Osilinus turbinatus - Turbinate monodont
Trochidae
►

Has a solid, globular shell, as wide as it is tall, on average about 2.5 centimeters. Lives in the Mediterranean and on the Atlantic coasts of Portugal and North Africa. A gregarious mollusk, it forms enormous populations on rocks in the midlittoral band.

Lischkeia alvinae
Trochidae
►

The pointed tubercles that traverse the middle band of each whorl give this trochid a particularly elegant appearance. It lives on the coasts of Japan and Taiwan. It is from 4 to 5 centimeters wide and is a uniform cream color.

Gibbula magus - Great topshell
Trochidae
►

The largest in the Gibbula genus, it reaches 3.5 centimeters in diameter. Lives in the Atlantic from Great Britain to Senegal and the Mediterranean, on detrital, sandy and muddy substrata in the infralittoral and circumlittoral bands. Whitish with red spots.

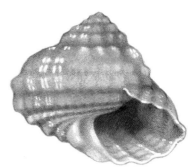

◄ **Tectus pyramis**
Trochidae

Robust and greenish-yellow in color, this trochid from the Indopacific is pagoda-shaped when young, quite different from the slender conical form it assumes as an adult. About 7 centimeters high, it lives in shallow waters on rocks near the reef.

◄ **Osilinus articulatus -** Tessellate trumpet
Trochidae

Abundant on rocks sheltered from waves, in the midlittoral band along the Mediterranean coasts. It reaches 3.5 centimeters in height and may vary in form and color; typically it has white spiral bands with reddish spots on a gray background.

◄ **Jujubinus exasperatus**
Trochidae Rough topshell

A small solid shell with an elegant form and quite variable ornamentation. It lives from Great Britain to Morocco to the Mediterranean from phanerogam meadows to coral environments. Fairly common, it reaches 1.5 centimeters in height.

Gibbula divaricata - Open topshell
Trochidae

Extremely common throughout the Mediterranean, especially where the rocks of the midlittoral band are protected from waves. Rarely exceeds 2 centimeters in height. It has a distinctive deep suture that makes the last whorl look detached.

Gibbula ardens
Flaming top
Trochidae

Common in the Mediterranean, it lives in meadows of dwarf Zostera seagrasses and algae. Reaches 1.7 centimeters in diameter. Apex is pointed, often rose-colored. Ornamentation consists of small spiral cords, from 4 to 7 on the last whorl, often duplicated by an edging.

Clanculus pharaonius
Trochidae

This is one of the most common and graceful shells that can be collected in the sand among rocky formations in the Indian Ocean. Reaches 2.5 centimeters in width. It has distinctive small beading in alternating colors.

Clanculus corallinus - Coral topshell
Trochidae

Graceful Mediterranean shell, bright red sometimes tending to brown. About one centimeter in size. Lives in rocky infralittoral and circumlittoral areas. More frequent in warm waters, but never very common.

Cittarium pica
Trochidae

This solid trochid is common in the tidal areas of the Caribbean islands and is prized by local populations as a food source. Its height and width vary from 5 to 12 centimeters. The shell is yellowish white with blackish purple spots.

Cantharidus eximius
Trochidae

Lives in the tidal area up to about forty meters deep in the Australian province, where it is rather common. Up to 4 centimeters high. It is red-brown in color with four greenish bands for each whorl.

Calliostoma zizyphinum
European painted topshell
Trochidae

Lives in the Mediterranean and off the Atlantic coasts of Europe, from the infralittoral band to the sandy and muddy floors of the circumlittoral band. Not common. Has a conical profile and shell that is rough at the apex and smooth at the base. An average of 3.5 centimeters in height.

Maurea cunninghami
Trochidae

Around ten beautiful top shells can be found in New Zealand, including this one, which can be distinguished by the size (7 centimeters) of the light shell, decorated by a series of narrow, dotted spiral bands. It can be found among rocks in shallow water.

Turbo marmoratus
Turbinidae

Large, massive shell from the Indopacific, where it lives from 4 to 20 meters deep. Reaches 17.5 centimeters in height. The bright green surface and iridescence of the aperture give it a lacquered appearance. Quite popular as a souvenir.

Bankivia fasciata
Trochidae

Lives along the southern coasts of Australia and is distinguished by its slender form and the variability of the elegant ornamentation with colored bands. Larger specimens, up to 3.5 centimeters in size, live along sandy, wave-swept coasts.

Bolma rugosa
Rough turbo
Turbinidae

Lives in the circumlittoral band of the Mediterranean and Atlantic southern Europe. When young, it has showy spines that disappear in adult shells. Reaches 5 centimeters in diameter. The calcareous operculum is considered a symbol of good luck.

Guildfordia yoka
Turbinidae

Has a depressed structure and reaches 10 centimeters in diameter. It is spiral-shaped, hexagonal near the apex, octagonal at the base, where angulations carry appendages as long as the diameter of the shell. Lives in Japan, where it is frequently found.

Angaria delphinus
Turbinidae

This Indopacific species lives in the circumlittoral band in coral habitats, and assumes different forms depending on the depth and currents in the area. Its spines may vary in length and shape. Up to 6 centimeters in diameter.

Astraea heliotropium
Turbinidae

Seen from above, this large turbo from New Zealand looks like a ten-pointed star, giving it its common name of star shell. It reaches 8 centimeters in diameter and lives in rather deep waters. It is somewhat uncommon.

Phasianella australis
Phasianellidae

With its 8 centimeters in height, it is the giant of the family that takes its name from the Latin for pheasant, due to its colors being similar to this bird. It lives in southern Australia and Tasmania, where it is common in shallow waters, among algae, on rocks in the infralittoral band.

Tricolia pullus - Pheasant shell
Tricoliidae

▶

Graceful and tiny (it rarely reaches one centimeter in length), it is frequent in the Mediterranean province at shallow depths among algae, on sandy floors. Its color ranges from pink to brown, with slightly undulating oblique flames.

◀ **Neritina communis**
Neritidae

The most colorful inhabitant of the mangroves, common throughout the Southwest Pacific. Its colors usually include yellow, white, black and all shades of pink, to brick red. The design is extremely varied. The apex is acute, and it is about 2 centimeters long. It is gathered in great quantities in the Philippines, and can often be found in souvenir shops.

Smaragdia viridis - Emerald nerite
Neritidae

▶

This tiny (maximum of 8 millimeters) shell is distinguished by the bright green color of its surface, adorned with white or purple markings. It is common from the Caribbean to the Mediterranean province. Frequent on algae at shallow depths.

◀ **Nerita textilis**
Neritidae

Robust, globular shell, adorned by solid spiral ribbing with alternating white and black spots. Found in the Indopacific province, where it is common on rocks in tidal areas. From 3.5 to 5 centimeters in size.

Nerita peloronta
Neritidae

▶

This is a very common species on reefs near the low tide mark, from Florida to Brazil. The inner lip of the aperture has white teeth surrounded by an orange or bright red spot. Reaches a maximum of 4 centimeters.

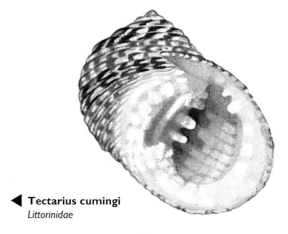

◀ **Tectarius cumingi**
Littorinidae

Common in the western Pacific, from Japan to New Caledonia. From 1.2 to 2.7 centimeters high, it has an especially graceful form due to the two robust spiral carinae on the last whorl. It is pink at the apex and creamy white on the rest.

Littorina neritoides
Reef snail
Littorinidae

▶

Forms large colonies in fissures in the rock, up to 2 meters above the high tide level. Up to 6 millimeters high, it is dark, black or brown with a narrow light band that is sometimes absent. Common in the Mediterranean and Atlantic Europe.

Littorina littorea
Littorinidae

Lives in Atlantic Europe and northeast America. Gray-black with black spiral bands, it reaches 3 centimeters in length. Quite common among the rocks of the lower midlittoral band, it is prized for its meat in France and England.

◀ **Rissoina spirata**
Rissoidae

An Indopacific species, it entered the Mediterranean from the Red Sea after the Suez Canal was opened. Reported on the coasts of Israel and the Tuscan archipelago. Lives in underwater meadows. Up to 10 millimeters high, it has a turriculate sculpture and is whitish in color.

Rissoa variabilis
Rissoidae

This elegant tapered shell is from 7 to 8 millimeters long, and is quite common on meadowy sea beds in European seas. It can be distinguished by its violet peristome and dotted brown spiral lines, sometimes alternating with solid lines. It has about ten ribs.

◀ **Rissoa violacea**
Rissoiade

It is abundant in Posidonia meadows throughout the Mediterranean, and its average length is a little under 6 millimeters. The upper whorls are smooth, while the last two have about ten wide ribs. Its color may vary, with spiral bands that may be flesh-colored, violet or purple. The inner lip has tones of violet.

Rissoa auriscalpum
Rissoidae

Has 7-8 flat axial ribs and a varicose lip. Whitish and semitransparent, it can reach 7-8 millimeters in height. It lives in European seas and can be quite abundant in Posidonia meadows in the infralittoral band.

◀ **Manzonia crassa** (formerly Folinia costata)
Rissoidae

Tiny shell that rarely reaches 3 millimeters in height. Bluish white, with 12-15 thin, oblique ribs that give it an elegant appearance. Lives in the Mediterranean in shallow waters, to about 15 meters in depth.

Cerithium vulgatum - Common cerith
Cerithidae

Robust shell with two spiral series of more or less raised tubercles on each whorl. Variable color, tending to brown. Up to 7 centimeters high. Quite common in rocky habitats in shallow waters in the Mediterranean and Atlantic.

Cerithium nodulosum ▶
Cerithidae

Solid, with a very marked spiral shape and chalky color. Three black spotted lines run across the tubercles. From 9 to 13 centimeters high, it is the giant of the family. Common in the Indopacific.

◀ **Bittium reticulatum**
Cerithidae

Ubiquitous species found in the seas of Europe, from a few meters to over one thousand meters in depth, in quite varied habitats. Abundant among vegetation. Has whorls traversed by three or four spiral circles and reaches a height of 13 millimeters.

Turritella duplicata ▶
Turritellidae

Slender shell with a spire of up to 15 whorls and 15 centimeters in length. The whorls may be more or less convex and are traversed by two spiral carinae. Lives on sandy and muddy floors of the Indian Ocean and feeds on detritus.

Turritella communis - Common European turritella
Turritellidae

Lives on sandy and slimy floors of the infralittoral band at a density of 70 individuals per square meter, along the European coasts of the North Sea to the Mediterranean. From 4 to 6 centimeters high.
◀ Convex whorls traversed by spiral, yellowish little ribs.

Mesalia opalina ▶
Turritellidae

Species from the Atlantic coasts of northwest Africa, recently introduced into the Mediterranean. Lives from 20 to 50 meters deep. White with red-brown axial flames. From 6 to 8 centimeters high.

Vermicularia spirata
Turritellidae

Lives among sponges and other colonial animals in shallow waters in the Caribbean. The first whorls curl regularly, but after a couple of
◀ centimeters elongate in irregular fashion. Frequent. Up to 13 centimeters high.

Tenagodus obtusus ▶
Siliquariidae

Similar to vermetids, but lives freely at shallow depths, with its first whorls in spiral form. A longitudinal furrow crosses the entire shell. Up to 10 centimeters high, diameter up to 11 millimeters. Mediterranean.

Vermetus triquetrus
Vermetidae

Lives attached to reefs in the midlittoral band and in trottoir formations. The unattached portion has a single, smooth crest. Diameter up to 6 millimeters. Quite common in the Mediterranean.

◀ Aporrhais pespelecani - Pelican's foot shell
Aporrhaidae

Normally has three robust digitations (which appear only in adults), plus that of the siphonal canal. Up to 5 centimeters in height, it lives in the Mediterranean, Celtic and Boreal provinces on muddy sea beds. Quite common, it is sold in fish markets.

Aporrhais occidentalis
Aporrhaidae

Lives from Labrador to North Carolina, at gradually greater depths as it moves south, under sand and mud, and feeds on detritus that it sucks up with its proboscis. It is from 4 to 6 centimeters high. Has a flared lip, but usually no digitation.

◀ Aporrhais elegantissima
Aporrhaidae

Lives on sandy and muddy floors in the circumlittoral band along the coasts of West Africa, where it is occasionally caught in fishermen's trawls. Prized for its particularly thin digitations. Around 5 centimeters high.

Varicospira cancellata
Strombidae

The dense axial ribbing traversing dense spiral striae gives this conch its characteristic reticular design. It is quite small for the family, from 2.5 to 3.5 centimeters. Frequent in the Philippines.

◀ Tibia insulaechorab
Strombidae

Lives in the Red Sea and north of the Indian Ocean, in the sand in tidal areas. Fifteen centimeters long, it has a very slender conical spire with a glossy, yellow-brown surface. From four to five short digitations on the outer lip.

Tibia fusus
Strombidae

The extremely large siphonal canal allows this conch to protect the very long siphon it uses to obtain food and oxygen while immersed in sand on the sea floor. Lives in the Philippines. Length 25 centimeters

Terebellum terebellum
Strombidae

▶

Unmistakable due to its projectile form, it is widespread in the Indopacific and is quite common. The last whorl is very elongated and has a narrow aperture that widens near the siphon area. It is from 4 to 5.5 centimeters high.

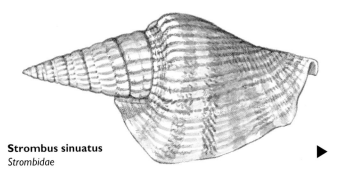

Strombus vittatus
Strombidae

Lives in the western Pacific near the coasts of Australia on sandy sea beds, up to about 40 meters in depth. Average in size (reaches 9 centimeters), with a very slender form, variable outside coloring with a white aperture.

◀

Strombus sinuatus
Strombidae

▶

Characteristic of this large species (height from 9 to 12 centimeters) is the sort of crest formed by 4 or 5 rounded lobes on the back side of the lip. It is white with red-brown decoration. Lives in the Indopacific.

◀ **Strombus pugilis**
Strombidae

Lives in shallow waters in the West Indies, where it is common. Color varies from creamy orange to salmon pink. Has robust spines on the margin of the whorls, with the longest usually located on the second row from the top. About 7.5 centimeters in height.

Strombus listeri
Strombidae

▶

Very elegant, once considered quite rare, but now somewhat frequent in the Indian Ocean. The very elongated spire occupies two fifths of the total length of 10 to 13 centimeters. The lip has a falcate flare.

◀ **Strombus goliath**
Strombidae

This is the giant of the family: with the spectacular wing-like flare of the outer lip of the aperture, it reaches 38 centimeters in length. It is light brown. Lives in Brazil and is quite rare.

Strombus gigas
Strombidae

▶

Common in the Caribbean from Florida to Venezuela, and known for its delicate meat and the ornamental use of the shell. Lives from 1.5 to 4.5 meters deep on sand and detritus among the algae on which it feeds.Exceeds 30 centimeters. Common.

Strombus gallus
Strombidae

The posterior elongation of the lip gives this shell from the Caribbean an elegant appearance. Color ranges from white to yellow, with red-brown spiral striae. Lives on sandy sea beds among algae. Not common. Thirteen centimeters in length.

►

◄ **Strombus costatus**
Strombidae

This large shell (reaches 18 centimeters high) lives in shallow waters, on sand and beds of algae, in bays and sheltered lagoons. Common from southern Florida to the West Indies to Mexico. Generally white-alabaster in color.

Strombus canarium
Strombidae

►

Quite variable in size and appearance, with color ranging from whitish to yellow-brown. Pointed spire, outside lip with thickened, smooth aperture. About 5 centimeters in length. Widespread in the Indopacific. Very common.

◄ **Lambis violacea**
Strombidae

The rarest and most graceful of the Lambis genus. It can be found on the island of Mauritius and other smaller islands off Madagascar. Interior of the aperture is purple, with a dozen digitations on the outside lip. Fifteen centimeters long.

Lambis scorpio
Strombidae

►

Lives on coarse sand and detritus in the infralittoral band throughout the Indopacific province. Not common. Length from 10 to 25 centimeters. The straight outer lip of the aperture is characteristic. Seven digitations.

◄ **Lambis millipeda**
Strombidae

Lives in the Southeast Pacific, from the Philippines to Java to New Guinea, in shallow waters in coral habitats. It is about 12 centimeters long, with a dozen principal digitations and a slight difference in form between males and females. Common

Lambis lambis
Strombidae

►

The most abundant of the genus, it lives in the Indopacific from the lower midlittoral band to 10 meters in depth. Feeds on algae growing on dead coral or rocks. Reaches 23 centimeters in length. Females are larger than males.

Lambis chirargra
Strombidae

Reaches 15 centimeters in length. The apex is pointed. The last whorl is deeply cut by spiral furrows that separate four large ribs. Six principal digitations. Lives in the Indopacific in the sediment around coral reefs.

Crepidula fornicata - Atlantic slipper
Crepidulidae

Lives attached to rocks, other shells, and the carapace of crustaceans. Ranges from 2 to 6.5 centimeters in length and has a form that varies depending on substratum. Originally from the American Atlantic, it has spread to European coasts and penetrated the Mediterranean.

Capulus hungaricus - Fool's cap
Capulidae

Has a curved apex from which extend radial ribs that cut across the growth lines. Lives attached to hard substrata, often on the valves of mussels. Reaches a diameter of 5 centimeters. Common in Europe from the North Sea to the Mediterranean.

Stellaria solaris
Xenophoridae

Characterized by 14 long spines. Rarely affixes other objects to the shell, except in the initial whorls. Reaches 9 centimeters in diameter. Lives in the circumlittoral and infralittoral bands of the Indian Ocean and the West Pacific.

Crepidula unguiformis - Fingernail slipper
Crepidulidae

Tiny, delicate, flattened but variable depending on substratum, it lives in shallow waters, where it adheres to the surface of other shells. Is whitish in color and has a smooth, glossy lower face. From 20 to 25 millimeters long. Mediterranean.

Calyptraea chinensis
Crepidulidae Chinese cup-and-saucer

Is very flat with a pointed apex. The diameter ranges from 10 to 20 millimeters. Lives in the infralittoral band, where it adheres to submerged objects, rocks and other shells. Lives on the two shores of the North Atlantic and in the Mediterranean.

Xenophora crispa
Xenophoridae

Has a flat cone form with a spire covered with various objects that the animal affixes to the sutures among the whorls, such as small shells, organic fragments and various minerals. Diameter between 3 and 4 centimeters. Lives in the West Central Mediterranean. Rare.

Cypraea pyrum
Cypraeidae

Widespread in the Mediterranean and on the west coast of Africa. Has a beautiful, varied color that runs from nut red to cream to violet, with banded or spotted markings. Lives in shallow waters. Rather common. From 2.5 to 5 centimeters in size.

Cypraea caurica
Cypraeidae

Indopacific species recently introduced to the eastern Mediterranean. Elongated, with color distinguished by three more or less light brown-olive bands with very dark spots. Common. From 2.5 to 5 centimeters in size.

Cypraea lurida
Cypraeidae

Common in the Mediterranean province, where it lives from 2 to 7 meters in depth. Nut colored with lighter bands on the back and two black spots on each of the two ends. The base is cream-colored. Rather frequent. From 3 to 5 centimeters in length.

Cypraea thersites
Cypraeidae

Swollen, almost globular form with white base and S-shaped aperture. The back is brown with black spots. Totally black specimens are frequent. Lives along the southern coasts of Australia, where it is not common. From 6 to 9 centimeters long.

Cypraea ziczac
Cypraeidae

Common and abundant throughout the Indopacific, where it lives in shallow waters in the infralittoral band. The back is cream-colored with white bands that create very characteristic V-shaped patterns. Small dark spots on the ends. From 1.2 to 2.3 centimeters in length.

Cypraea nigropunctata
Cypraeidae

Has an elongated, subcylindrical form and is small in size (from 2.3 to 3, 6 centimeters). The back is yellowish, covered with variable, nut-colored spots. There are two blackish spots on the two ends. Lives along the coasts of Peru, Ecuador and the Galapagos Islands.

Cypraea mus
Cypraeidae

Found along the Atlantic coasts of Venezuela and Colombia, where it is rather rare. Has a distinctive coloring around the dorsal band, with dark spots that create an irregular pattern on a sand-colored background. From 3 to 6 centimeters in size.

Cypraea moneta
Cypraeidae ▶

Since the dawn of civilization, this shell has been the one most commonly used for money and ornamental purposes. Has a rather irregular form, with color than runs from white to yellow to green, with a red line. Indopacific and Panamic. About 2.5 centimeters long.

Cypraea leucodon
Cypraeidae ▶

The white teeth on the cream-colored background of the aperture give this extremely rare cowry its name. Its habitat is unknown. It has been found in the Indian and Pacific oceans in the intestines of the fish that feed on it. From 7 to 8.5 centimeters in length.

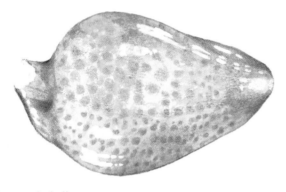

Cypraea isabella
Cypraeidae ▶

Lives in shallow waters throughout the Indopacific, and is very common. It is little more than 5 centimeters in length. It has two brownish-red spots on the ends: the beige or light gray shell is traversed by dark dotted or segmented lines.

Cypraea granulata
Cypraeidae ▶

Has unusual ornamentation for a cowry, with beading that runs from the back to the side margin. Its color varies, with little spots that range from brown to orange to lilac. Varies in length from 2 to 4 centimeters. Lives in Hawaii and Midway.

◀ Cypraea mappa
Cypraeidae

Has a swollen, somewhat pear-shaped form. The pattern on its back is beautiful and varies from individual to individual, with a white stripe that branches out in various directions, resembling a map. Widespread and common in the Indopacific. From 5 to 9 centimeters long.

◀ Cypraea hesitata
Cypraeidae

Lives in deep waters in Southeast Australia and Tasmania and is fairly common. Has a white, sinuous aperture that widens in front, while the cream-colored back has irregular brown spots. Ten centimeters long.

◀ Cypraea guttata
Cypraeidae

Lives in the Indopacific, where it is very rare. Has beautiful red stripes around the aperture and edges, and large, infrequent spots on the cream-colored back, sometimes traversed by a lighter stripe. It is about 5 centimeters long.

Cypraea fultoni
Cypraeidae

▶

It was considered extremely rare until the late 1980's, when its habitat off Mozambique was discovered. It is 8 centimeters long, with brown spots on the light background of the base, while the back has a beautiful print pattern.

Cypraea depressa
Cypraeidae

▶

Oval-shaped and average in size (from 2.5 to 5.5 centimeters), with a beautiful spotted pattern on the back, with zigzag lines running into brown areas. The base is white with brown spots. Lives in the Indopacific in rough waters.

◀ **Cypraea diluculum**
Cypraeidae

Small (from 1.3 to 3.2 centimeters long), and quite lovely, it lives along the entire eastern coast of Africa and islands in the Indian Ocean. Quite common, it takes refuge under rocks and dead corals on rocky sea beds in shallow water. Its design is quite characteristic, consisting of longitudinal zigzag bands.

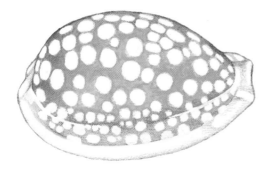

Cypraea cervus
Cypraeidae

▶

The back of this large shell (9 to 15 centimeters in size) is a beautiful dappled tawny color, sometimes traversed by a light stripe. The aperture is wider at the front. Lives in the infralittoral band from Florida to Mexico. Rather common.

◀ **Cypraea cribraria**
Cypraeidae

Elongated, with its back speckled with white circles that stand out against the light nut-colored background. The base and margin of the lips are white. Lives in the Indopacific and is relatively common. Length: 2.5 centimeters.

Cypraea capensis
Cypraeidae
Oval-shaped and 2.5 centimeters long, it lives near South Africa. Ornamentation consists of a series of thin, attractive transverse wrinkles on a pink to brown background. Nut-colored central spots. Rather frequent.

◀ **Cypraea caputserpentis**
Cypraeidae

One of the most common shells in the Indopacific. Found from Japan to Hawaii, Tahiti, and Africa. White spots stand out on a brown network, while two white spots at the ends interrupt the dark band along the margins. Three centimeters long.

Cypraea aurantium
Cypraeidae ▶

Once the insignia of the kings of the Fiji Islands, it is even now one of the most coveted of shells. From 6 to 10 centimeters long. Its color is unmistakable: the back is golden orange, with a white base. Lives in caves of coral formations in the Pacific. Extremely rare.

◀ **Cypraea armeniaca**
Cypraeidae

Has an oval form, with the golden yellow surface scattered with little dark spots and lines. Reaches a maximum of 8 centimeters in length and is endemic in the waters of Australia. Extremely rare.

Cypraea argus
Cypraeidae ▶

Cylindrical in form, it is spattered with eyes like the mythological monster that gives it its name. Three transverse bands and two spots on each lip complete the ornamentation. It is 8 centimeters long. Lives in the Indopacific, where it is rather rare.

Cypraea arabica
Cypraeidae

The back of this Indopacific shell is traversed by light lines on a brown background variously intersected by transverse lines, resembling Arabic script. It lives in shallow waters under dead
◀ corals and rocks. Common. From 3 to 8 centimeters in size.

Cypraea annulus
Cypraeidae ▶

Along with Cypraea moneta, it was for centuries used as currency in vast areas of Asia and Africa. Blue-gray inside the gold ring, and cream-colored on the rest of the shell. About 2 centimeters in length. Indopacific. Common.

Volva volva
Ovulidae

Elongated with a light but robust structure, with no denticles. Lives in the Indopacific, usually associated with soft corals on sea beds off the reef. Color ranges from pink to beige. Quite common, it is
◀ about 12 centimeters in length.

Ovula ovum
Ovulidae ▶

Very shiny shell, milk white on the outside, while the interior visible through the aperture is deep red. Lives in the Indopacific in the upper infralittoral band, among the sponges and black corals on which it feeds. An average of 7.5 centimeters in length.

Trivia monacha
Triviidae

Species common from the North Sea to the Mediterranean. Lives on hard substrata at modest depths, and feeds primarily on sea squirts. Up to 12 millimeters high. Its glossy, corrugated back has from three to four nut-colored spots on a cream-colored background.

▶

Lamellaria perspicua.
Lamellariidae

◀

This little mollusk with a whitish, transparent, ear-shaped shell with a large aperture, lives in association with colonies of sea squirts, among whom it lays its eggs. The diameter ranges from 12 to 16 millimeters. Mediterranean and Atlantic.

Neverita josephinia
Neverita moon snail
Naticidae

▶

Flattened, porcelain-like shell with a columellar callus that nearly closes off the umbilicus. White-yellow in color, with a gray-blue spiral band. Mediterranean species common in sands in the infralittoral band. From 3 to 4 centimeters in diameter.

Natica stercusmuscarum (formerly Naticarius millepunctatus)
Fly-specked moon
Naticidae

◀

Mediterranean species. Characteristically, it has many chestnut-colored little spots that stand out against a very light background. There are, however, albino specimens and those with uniform or banded colors. From 3 to 5 centimeters in diameter. Rather common.

Natica canrena
Naticidae

▶

This beautiful naticid, with its shell adorned by four intersecting, cream-colored bands with axial flames, lives in the sand at shallow depths, from North Carolina to the West Indies. From 2.5 to 6.4 centimeters in height.

Natica lineata
Naticidae

◀

Lives on the sandy and muddy sea beds of the coastal Indian Ocean and West Pacific, from Taiwan to the northern Philippines. Small in size (from 2 to 3 centimeters), it has a cupola-shaped spire that is quite distinct from the last whorl. Its design includes more or less zigzag axial bands that range from orange to brown in color, on a whitish background.

Euspira catena - Chain snail
Naticidae

▶

A uniform light nut color, with little spots that form a chain pattern in the suture. The columellar callus is white. Lives on sandy seabeds in the infralittoral band, in the Mediterranean and the Atlantic. Reaches 5 centimeters in height.

Tonna tessellata
Tonnidae

▶

Very common species in the West Pacific. Has a flattened spire from which the slightly pointed apex emerges. The very deep spiral striae are characteristic. Cream-colored with chestnut-colored spots. From 6 to 13 centimeters high.

◀ **Tonna galea** - Helmet ton
Tonnidae

Cosmopolitan species not found in cold seas. It lives on sandy or detrital floors of the infralittoral and circumlittoral bands. The shell is large, light and fragile, with colors that vary from yellow to cream to brown. From 10 to 15 centimeters in height.

Ficus ventricosus
Ficidae

▶

Lives in the Panamic province and reaches medium to large size. The pear-shaped appearance is typical of the family, but its form is rendered interesting by a regular succession of spiral ribs in three different heights. The color is light nut brown.

◀ **Phalium areola**
Cassidae

Has a rather slender structure and a thin network on the spire and first part of the last whorl. Color ranges from pink to light nut brown, with four series of chestnut-colored spots. From 5-10 centimeters high. Common in the Indopacific.

Cypraeacassis testiculus
Cassidae

▶

Lives along the eastern coasts of America and Africa (where, however, it is rare). Has a particular mosaic sculpture created by axial stripes intersecting with spiral stripes. The dorsal color ranges from nut brown to violet. Height runs from 3 to 9 centimeters.

Cypraeacassis rufa
Cassidae

Since ancient times, this shell was most commonly used to make cameos, using the contrast between the red-orange and the cream of the shell's different layers. Common in the Indopacific. Height ◀ ranges from 10 to 15 centimeters.

Galeodea echinophora - Mediterranean rugose (spiny) bonnet
Cassidae

▶

Up to 10 centimeters in height, it is extremely common in the Mediterranean province, and is even sold in fish markets. It is nut brown on the outside, and white in the aperture. Large spiral ridges with nodules traverse the entire shell.

Distorsio anus ▶
Ranellidae

The shell has a truly singular form, with asymmetrical, eccentrically developed whorls on the spire. The edges of the aperture are quite irregular. It lives in the coral reefs of the Indopacific. From 4 to 8 centimeters in height.

Cymathium corrugatum - Corrugated triton ▶
Ranellidae

When the periostracum that forms a velvety brown covering is removed, the shell is white with nut-colored, deeply indented spiral furrows. Its height ranges from 6 to 9 centimeters. Lives on sandy beds of the Mediterranean. Not present in the Adriatic.

◀ **Cymathium rubeculum**
Ranellidae

One of the smallest and most graceful of the Ranellidae: its height ranges from 3.5 to 5 centimeters. The surface, in various shades of red, is covered with beading and traversed by varices. Lives in the Indopacific, Australia, and America, near coral reefs.

◀ **Charonia lampas** (formerly nodifera) - Knobbed triton
Ranellidae

A giant among gastropods (reaches a height of 40 centimeters), used to make horns in ancient times. Is widely distributed in warm seas, not including the Americas. It is found in the western part of the Mediterranean up to a depth of 200 meters.

Ranella olearia (formerly Argobuccinum giganteum)
Wandering triton
Ranellidae

A large (from 15 to 21 centimeters), robust and light shell with a vast distribution, from the eastern Atlantic to the Mediterranean, South Africa and Australia, on sea beds in the circumlittoral band. Has two series of axial varices in the form of ridges. ▶

◀ **Bursa scrobiculator**
Bursidae

Has a very distinctive aperture, with toothed and furrowed inner edges. Tawny color with darker spots. The varices are often knobby, but may be absent. From 7 to 9 centimeters in height. Lives in the Mediterranean province.

Bursa crumena ▶
Bursidae

This elegant representative of an almost exclusively tropical member of the gastropod family lives in the Indopacific. It is pink with violet tones. Sculpture is rather variable. From 5 to 9 centimeters high.

Monophorus perversus (formerly Triphora perversa)
Triphoridae

Has a sinistral shell like all triphorids, and is common from Norway to the Mediterranean. Lives under rocks in the tidal area up to 80 meters in depth. Has 16 to 18 spires adorned with three rows of beading. From 2 to 2.5 centimeters high.

Opalia funicolata (formerly Opalia crenimarginata)
Epitoniidae

Lives at the lower edge of the tidal area, at the base of sea anemones from the genus Anthopleura, from southern California to Panama. It is from 10 to 19 millimeters high and is opaque white in color. The ribbing is prominent in the first whorls, and then diminishes.

Opalia crenata
Epitoniidae

Has a white, thick shell and lives in the Mediterranean province, where it is extremely rare. About 2 centimeters high. It has often been found in association with the sea anemone Anemonia sulcata in shallow waters on coarse, wave-swept sand.

Epitonium scalare - Precious wentletrap
Epitoniidae

This is one of the legendary rarities in shell collecting. Today, it is fished in the Philippines from deep sea beds, using trawls, but as fragile as it is, it is difficult to bring it up intact. The whorls just barely adhere to each other. It is from 5 to 7 centimeters high.

Epitonium commune
Epitoniidae

Lives on sandy sea beds in the Mediterranean and the Atlantic in Western Europe, feeding on coelenterates, especially sea anemones. An average of 4 centimeters high, the shell has 10-12 spires, with nine axial lamellae. Cream colored with brown bands.

Janthina janthina
Janthinidae

Pelagic, cosmopolitan species (except for polar seas). It floats with the currents, using a raft of tiny bubbles of mucus. It feeds on pelagic coelenterates like the by-the-wind-sailor (Vellella). Four centimeters high, the shell is violet with tones of white.

Thais congulata
Muricidae

A South African species of modest dimensions (2.5 to 4 centimeters), it is nevertheless unmistakable due to its truly unique sculpture. Each whorl has two quite raised whitish cords, except for the last one, which has three. In the spaces between the cords, there are slightly upraised spiral striae. It is pink in color.

Thais lacera (Formerly haemastoma) - Red-mouth purpura
Muricidae

Lives in the Mediterranean and Atlantic (from Africa to the Bay of Biscay in Africa) in algae-rich reefs, where it preys on bivalves. The more or less knobby shell is often covered with encrustations. The aperture is orange. Up to 8 centimeters high.

Rapana venosa - Sea turnip
Muricidae

This Indopacific murex, which preys on bivalves, as do most members of its family, made news in the early 1960's when it began to invade the Mediterranean. Reaches 12 centimeters in height. The aperture is orange.

Typhinellus sowerby
Muricidae

Found, but is not frequent, on coral sea beds in the Mediterranean and West Africa. Slender and small (no more than 2.2 centimeters), this shell is noteworthy for the significant wing-shaped flare of the lip of the aperture.

Hexaplex brassica (formerly Phyllonotus brassica)
Muricidae

Large murex from the Panamic province: may exceed 15 centimeters in height, and larger specimens with more interesting ornamentation are dredged from deep sea beds. White with three brown spiral bands. The aperture is pink.

Pteropurpura plorator
Muricidae

Comes from the southeast coasts of Japan and is prized for its ornamentation. Three prominent varices traverse the shell axially, creating falcate lobes. The lip of the aperture is flared. It is about 3.5 to 5 centimeters high.

Nucella lapillus
Muricidae

Active predator of mussels, and common in the tidal area along the coasts of Europe and North America, from Labrador to New York. Varies in size (from 2 to 5 centimeters), color (from whitish to dark brown) and sculpture, which may be more or less prominent.

Ocenebra erinaceus
Muricidae Sting winkle

Lives on rocks and port structures, from the tidal zone to shallow depths, and is common on European coasts from the North Sea to the Mediterranean. Feeds on bivalves. Up to 6 centimeters high, with a thick lip adorned by wide crests.

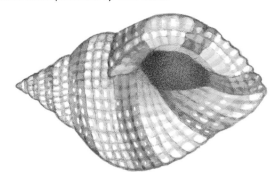

Hexplex radix
Muricidae

▶

Lives along the Pacific coasts from Panama to Ecuador. The surface is white, but the numerous black spines that run from the axial ribs, closely pressed together, give it a blackish appearance. Up to 15 centimeters in height.

Pterynotus elongatus
Muricidae

▶

The broad, wing-shaped flares and height of the spire give this murex from Japan and the Indopacific a surprising appearance. It is white in color. Lives on detrital and coral sea beds in the open sea. Reaches 8 centimeters in length.

Latiaxis pilsbryi
Muricidae

The most prized of the Latiaxis of Japan, which are the most beautiful of the genus. It is dredged from deep waters, has a diameter of 4 centimeters and is rare. The tabular spire with flattened spines is characteristic. It is pure white.

Hexaplex trunculus (formerly Trunculariopsis)
Trunculus murex
Muricidae

▶

Frequent from the midlittoral band to a depth of eight meters, on various types of sea beds, in the Mediterranean and Atlantic in the Mediterranean province. The Phoenicians caught it for its purple dye, but today it is used for food. Reaches a length of 8 centimeters.

◀ **Murex pecten** - Venus comb murex
Muricidae

This is one of the wonders of the realm of mollusks, due to the elegance of its very delicate spines. It is common in the Indopacific on relatively deep sea beds, and is dredged by fishing boats. Up to 15 centimeters long.

◀ **Morula uva**
Muricidae

A gregarious species: can be found on midlittoral or infralittoral rocks in the Indopacific, usually in groups, or at least in pairs. Up to 2.5 centimeters high. The last whorl has six rows of black tubercles, while the aperture is violet.

◀ **Homalocantha anatomica**
Muricidae

This murex, once rare but now regularly collected by fishermen in the open sea off the Philippines, looks like an abstract sculpture made of a little pile of bones. The varices are arranged on three axial rows. About 4-5 centimeters high.

Haustellum haustellum
Muricidae

The extremely long siphonal canal, extended for over half the shell's total length (from 6 to 15 centimeters) characterizes this Indopacific murex, which seems to prefer sandy or muddy beds at the mouths of rivers.

►

◄ **Drupa morum**
Muricidae

It is 2.5 centimeters high and globular in appearance. There are three or four rows of blackish spines on the last whorl. The sinuous aperture is purple, with white denticles. Common on Indopacific littoral reefs exposed to waves.

Concholepas peruvianus - Loco
Muricidae Loco

Lives along the coasts of Peru. Looks like a capulid and adheres to the rocks of the midlittoral and infralittoral band like a limpet. Harvested in great numbers for food purposes, it is now a protected species. Reaches 9 centimeters in diameter.

►

◄ **Chicoreus palmarosae**
Muricidae

Rare and elegant, it is found in the Indopacific. Its ornate ramifications are arranged in three axial rows that also run along the siphonal canal. The apex and the upper part of the ramifications are pink. It is 7 to 12 centimeters high.

Bolinus brandaris (formerly Murex) - Purple dye murex
Muricidae

►

Lives from 5 to 80 meters in depth and is common from the Mediterranean to West Africa. The Phoenicians obtained their famous purple dye from it. Today it is collected for food. Reaches a length of 9 centimeters and has widely varying ornamentation.

◄ **Acanthina punctulata**
Muricidae

This little murex frequents reefs in the upper midlittoral band in California. From 2.2 to 3.8 centimeters high, it has an ornate surface with spiral carinae that intersect with small axial ridges to form a brown checkerboard pattern.

Coralliophila meyendorffi - Lamellose coral snail
Muricidae

►

Is part of a subfamily (Coralliphilinae) of gastropods with no radula, as they feed by sucking the tissues of coelenterates. It is common in the Mediterranean and the Atlantic at shallow depths. It is 3.5 centimeters high and has a rose-colored aperture.

Pollia dorbigny (formerly Cantharus d'orbignyi) - Cantharus
Muricidae

Distinguished by very accentuated spiral stripes and convex whorls. Lives in the Mediterranean on sea beds rich with marine vegetation. The spire is brown with a white area. The aperture is white with violet spots. It is 15-18 millimeters in height.

Penion dilatatus
Muricidae

Members of the Penion genus are carnivorous cold water whelks that live in southern Australia and New Zealand. They are caught in fishing trawls. Dilatatus is up to 18 centimeters long and has a knobby carina in the middle of its whorls.

◀ **Pisania striata** (formerly maculosa)
Tinted cantharus or striate pisania
Muricidae

Very common in the Mediterranean and Portugal, at shallow depths, especially in areas rich with marine vegetation. About 3 centimeters long, its color varies from white to nut brown to olive green, with a light central band.

Buccinum undatum - Common northern whelk
Muricidae

Also common in the shallow waters along both coasts of the North Atlantic. In the Mediterranean, relict families live on at great depths. It feeds on dead or dying animals. Color runs from white to brown, height to 11 centimeters.

◀ **Neptunea contraria**
Muricidae

A sinistral shell species, common in the seas of northern Europe. It is gray, with a surface traversed by dense spiral striae. From 7 to 11 centimeters high. Is sometimes caught in fishing boat trawls.

Babylonia canaliculata
Muricidae

The spire, with its almost vertical whorls and deeply incised suture, resembles the mythical Tower of Babel that gave its name to the genus. Lives on sandy infralittoral sea beds in the Indian Ocean and is fairly common. From 4 to 6.5 centimeters high.

◀ **Buccinulum corneum** - Common whelk
Muricidae

Lives in the Mediterranean on sandy or muddy sea beds from 5 to 60 meters deep, feeding on carrion but also other mollusks, worms and small living crustaceans. Its shell is beige with chestnut flames. About 5 centimeters in height.

Mitrella scripta ▶
Columbellidae

A Mediterranean species found in rocky habitats among photophilic algae and on sponges. The shell, about 2 centimeters in length, is brilliant white with reddish speckles. The columella and interior of the lip are orange.

◀ **Columbella rustica** - Rustica dove-shell
Columbellidae

Lives in the Mediterranean and Atlantic to Angola. It is common on vegetation-rich reefs, where it feeds on algae and detritus. Its color varies, but the thick, toothed lip makes it unmistakable. It is 2 centimeters high.

Nassarius mutabilis (formerly Sphaeronassa mutabilis) ▶
Mutable nassa
Muricidae

Species common throughout the Mediterranean province, sometimes abundant. In the Adriatic, it is sold in fish markets. Lives on sandy and oozy sea beds and feeds on carrion, as do the others of its genus. From 2.5 to 4 centimeters high. Cream-colored with reddish flames.

◀ **Nassarius albus**
Muricidae

Tiny shell, from 6 to 13 millimeters long, white with a chestnut band under the suture. Prominent axial ribbing and faint spiral ridges. Lives in the sand up to a depth of 30 meters, from North Carolina to the West Indies.

Nassarius reticulatus (formerly Hinia reticulata) ▶
Common netted dogwhelk
Muricidae

Lives on shallow sandy sea beds where it feeds on dead animals, which it can smell from a distance of 30 meters. Widespread in the Atlantic, from Norway to Morocco, and in the Mediterranean to the Black Sea. An average of 3 centimeters high, with cancellate ornamentation

◀ **Cyclope neritea** - Nerite-like dog whelk
Muricidae

Has a flat form, with the lower portion completely covered by a white callus. The upper part is brown, with a variety of flames. It is common in the Mediterranean on sandy, shallow sea beds, including littoral ponds. It is 10-15 millimeters in diameter.

Bullia armata ▶
Muricidae

This representative of the subfamily Nassariinae is frequent on sandy sea beds along the coasts of South America, from Brazil to Argentina. It is distinguished by the beautiful crown of tubercles running along the spire. It is 3.5 to 5 centimeters high.

Bullia vittata
Muricidae

▶

This is a small necrophage from the sandy and muddy coasts of the Indian Ocean. It is from 3.4 to 4.5 centimeters in size, and has a very elegant, slender form. The beginning of each whorl has a double row of beading, followed by a series of faint spiral striae. Its color ranges from cream to pink.

Melongena corona
Melongenidae

▶

Lives in the mud or muddy sand of the midlittoral band, in lagoons and often in mangrove forests, feeding on carrion or preying on bivalves. Quite variable (length from 2.5 to 20 centimeters), including in ornamentation. Common in the Caribbean.

◀ **Syrinx aruanus**
Melongenidae

This is a giant among gastropods, reaching 60 centimeters in length. Lives in Australia, on shallow muddy sea beds, but can be found at up to 60 meters in depth. It is an extremely active predator, especially of other mollusks. Its flesh is edible.

Pleuroploca gigantea
Muricidae

▶

This is one of the largest gastropods, reaching a half meter in height. Preys on other gastropods (by blocking the operculum before it closes) and bivalves. Lives in the Caribbean on sand and mud in the infralittoral band to a depth of 6 meters.

◀ **Busycon contrarium**
Melongenidae

Sinistral, fusiform shell, with low spire and final whorl that ends in a slightly bent siphonal canal. Dimension varies greatly, from 6.5 to 40 centimeters. Lives in the sand to a depth of 3 meters, from North Carolina to Texas.

Fusinus rostratus - Spindle shell
Muricidi Spindle shell

▶

Lives in the circumlittoral and on the continental slope, on sea beds abundant in organic detritus. It is common in the Mediterranean. The shell reaches 5 centimeters in size and is distinguished by a siphonal canal longer than the aperture and prominent axial ribs.

◀ **Latirus craticulatus**
Muricidae

Common in the Indopacific. The shell differs from those characteristic of the genus Latirus and approaches those of the whelks, with a long spire and short siphonal canal. It is from 4-5 centimeters long and has white and reddish lines.

Fasciolaria lignaria - Wooden fasciolaria, knotty tulip
Muricidae

This predator lives in the Mediterranean, from shallow waters to significant depths, preferably on sand and mud, but also on reefs. The shell is about 5 centimeters long and can easily be distinguished by its large white nodules.

Fasciolaria hunteria
Muricidae

Found at depths of from 1 to 12 meters on sea beds of muddy sand or beds of algae, where it preys on other mollusks. It is common from North Carolina to Texas. Its color varies from blue-green to light mauve, with a dark band. From 7 to 8 centimeters high.

Voluta musica
Volutidae

This lovely volute, from 3 to 9 centimeters high, has a beautiful pattern of lines and spots that resembles a musical staff. It lives on coral sand in the Caribbean from 30 centimeters to 6 meters in depth.

Melo aethiopicus
Volutidae

Large oval shell, beige-pink in color, with a spire visible only from above because it is embedded in the crown-like ornamentation of the last whorl. From 14 to 25 centimeters high, it lives in the Indopacific from the Philippines to northeastern Australia.

Lyria cumingii
Volutidae

Small volute (maximum 3 centimeters in size) that lives near Panama. Can be found in sublittoral habitats to 20 meters in depth, on soft sea beds. A series of small tubercles in increasing size accompanies the whorls.

Harpulina arausiaca
Volutidae

A rare volute that lives along the northern coast of Ceylon and the coast of southern India, on sea beds about 20 meters deep. From 6 to 9 centimeters in size, it has a pattern of orange rectangles on cream white that resembles a wall of bricks.

Halia priamus
Volutidae

A thin, light, very elegant shell with a glossy, light nut-colored surface with darker bands and a series of little square spots. Lives 40 meters deep and beyond, in the Atlantic from Vigo, Spain to Mauritania. From 5 to 7.5 centimeters high.

Ericusa sowerby
Volutidae

Collected by trawls in southeastern Australia on soft sea beds from 20 to 160 meters deep, and is fairly common. Has a very slender structure and can reach 25 centimeters high. Its pattern varies greatly, with more or less densely arranged lines.

Cymbium olla
Volutidae

Lives between 45 and 90 meters in depth, from the coast of Spain to Senegal. Its surface is opaque, and the aperture is quite wide and flared. Its color varies from creamy pink to nut brown. Its height ranges from 9 to 11 centimeters.

Cymbium cymbium
Volutidae

Large members of the Cymbium genus are regularly fished for food along the coast of Africa from Morocco to Senegal. This species has an almost cylindrical shell with a prominent carina behind the last whorl. It is from 10 to 15 centimeters high.

Cymbiola vespertilio
Volutidae

This Indopacific volute is the most common but also one of the most beautiful of the family, due to the variety of colors and the bat wing pattern that gives it its name. Lives on sand up to 20 meters in depth. From 5 to 11 centimeters high.

Cymbiola imperialis
Volutidae

Always prized for its extraordinary crown-like ornamentation, formed of spines in increasing height located in the middle of the whorls. Lives in the Philippines on sandy sea beds, from 2 to 20 meters deep. It is from 8 to 20 centimeters high.

Amoria undulata
Volutidae

The genus Amoria lives only in Australian waters (and in the far south of Indonesia), on sandy sea beds of the infralittoral and circumlittoral bands. The glossiness and wavy pattern of these shells make them quite beautiful. It is from 7 to 10 centimeters long.

Alcithoe swainsoni
Volutidae

Lives in New Zealand on sea beds of sand or mud, from 2 to 90 meters deep. This family has the habit of remaining buried in the substratum by day and coming out at night in search of prey. It is from 9 to 22 centimeters long, with variable colors.

Harpa harpa
Harpidae ▶

Can be distinguished by other members of the genus by the very marked contrast in the spectacular tapestry pattern that adorns the shell of these predators that live on sandy sea beds. There are three spots on the columella. It is from 5 to 7 centimeters high. Southwest Pacific.

◀ ## Turbinella pyrum (formerly Xancus pyrum)
Vasidae

This is the sacred shell of the Hindus, who use it in temple ceremonies as a symbol of Krishna. Sinistral specimens are highly prized. Has a pear-shaped structure, is from 5 to 15 centimeters high and is frequently fished from the sea beds of the Gulf of Bengal.

Vasum muricatum
Vasidae ▶

Has a massive biconical shell and lives in the Caribbean, in shallow waters up to 10 meters deep, where it preys on worms and other mollusks. The columella has four or five prominent folds. It is about 8 centimeters high.

◀ ## Columbarium pagoda
Vasidae

It has a very slender structure with a long siphonal canal, and is common along the coasts of Japan. Its height varies from 5 to 8 centimeters. A crown of spines appears along the carina of the indentations. There is a second carina near the aperture.

Oliva splendidula
Olividae ▶

Lives in the Panamic province, is from 4 to 5 centimeters high and is rather rare. The spire is distinct, the suture evident. The color is quite interesting: two triangle-shaped chestnut bands and little spots with a tail run across the cream-colored background.

◀ ## Oliva peruviana
Olividae

Has an oval shape, a distinct spire and hump near the last whorl. It may be uniformly chestnut in color, but more beautiful specimens are cream-colored with zigzag axial chestnut-colored stripes. Lives in Peru and Chile. From 4 to 5 centimeters high.

Oliva lignaria
Olividae ▶

Species common in the Indian Ocean and West Pacific, including northern Australia. An average of 6 centimeters high, it has a subcylindrical form. Its color is highly variable, as is its pattern, which may be indistinct or very marked.

Baryspira urasima ▶
Olividae

Lives along the coasts of Japan and remains buried in the sand, with only the siphon emerging to detect the presence of the carrion on which it feeds. Is beautifully colored, with a nut-colored band on cream background.

Marginella rosea ◀
Marginellidae

Slender, with a rather wide aperture, from 20 to 35 millimeters high, and rather common along the coasts of South and East Africa. Its cream-colored surface is adorned with an intricate pattern of little pink spots, lines and dots.

Cryptospira elegans ▶
Marginellidae

Small (25 - 35 millimeters) and oval, this margin shell from the Bay of Bengal is a true jewel in the elegance of its pattern. The light gray final whorl is traversed by dark gray spiral bands interrupted by axial bands. The aperture is chestnut-colored.

Volvarina avena ◀
Marginellidae

Lives among and under rocks and corals at the edge of the low tide mark to a depth of 90 meters, and is common from North Carolina to Brazil. From 10 to 16 millimeters high, it is pink or yellow in color, with two bands on the last whorl.

Glabella adansoni ▶
Marginellidae

Lives on the sandy sea beds of West Africa, where this family of gastropods is very well represented. Has a distinct and developed spire. From 2 to 3.5 centimeters high, it has a pattern formed by clear axial lines and spiral spots.

Mitra zonata - Bicolor miter ◀
Mitridae

Found in the Mediterranean province, at a minimum of 30 meters deep (in the Adriatic) to over 1000 deep in the Atlantic. Once considered extremely rare, it now seems to be more common. Slender, up to 10 centimeters long, it has a light nut-colored band on a dark background.

Mitra stictica (formerly pontificalis) ▶
Mitridae

Lives in coral sediment and under blocks of dead coral, and is common throughout the Indopacific. About 6 centimeters high, it has a ladder-like profile, with cylindrical whorls and a suture that forms a little channel. Groups of red spots form irregular spirals.

Mitra mitra
Mitridae

Lives in coral sediment, where it is easy to find by following the furrow it leaves as it moves. It is common throughout the Indopacific, and may reach 15 centimeters high. Square red markings on a white surface, ivory-colored aperture. ▶

Mitra belcheri
Mitridae

◀ This is the most beautiful miter in the Panama province, and is collected on the Pacific coast of Mexico. It is up to 12 centimeters high and rather rare. The slender, dark spire is traversed by a single white spiral furrow, while the aperture is salmon-colored.

Cancilla filaris - File miter
Mitridae

This predator (3 centimeters in size) lurks in coral sands and rough detritus at shallow depths. Like all miters, it has a gland that produces a paralyzing poison. It lives in the Indopacific. Its color runs from cream to yellow. ▶

Vexillum subdivisum
Costellariidae

◀ Has a slender, spindle-shaped form, with somewhat rounded individual whorls and a rather deep suture. Sinuous axial ribs frame little rectangular markings formed of spiral striae. From 3.5 to 5 centimeters high, it lives in the Indopacific, where it is not frequent.

Vexillum sanguisugum
Costellariidae

Has a distinctive surface covered with beading formed by the intersection of spiral striae with rounded axial ribs. Standing out on the white background is a little spiral band formed of pairs of red dotted lines on the ribs. It is 35 millimeters high and lives in the Indopacific. ▶

Vexillum ebenus (formerly Mitra ebenus) - Ebony miter
Costellariidae

◀ Lives among the vegetation of rocky sea beds or hard substrata in the Mediterranean. It is about 3 centimeters high. It is very dark or black, with a pale line running along the whorls. The columella has four little white folds.

Cancellaria foveolata
Cancellariidae

▶ This small, common South African species, from 2 to 3 centimeters high, has a ladder-like profile that is rather unusual for a cancellarid. The spiral sculpture is barely perceptible. Its color may vary, but always includes a darker band.

Cancellaria cancellata
Cancellariidae

Lives in the Senegalese and western Mediterranean province, on detrital or muddy sea beds in the infralittoral and circumlittoral bands. About 3 centimeters high, it has a distinctive cancellate sculpture and a brown band on cream background.

Conus textile
Conidae

All members of the Conus genus are voracious predators who paralyze their prey by injecting them with poison from a dart on the proboscis. This species, from 4 to 13 centimeters high, is even dangerous to humans. Lives in the sand in shallow waters in the Indopacific, where it is common.

Conus vexillum
Conidae

The shell is robust but surprisingly light. Lives hidden among corals under the low tide mark on the side of the reef exposed to the waves, in the Indopacific. Reaches a height of 15 centimeters. It is brown with white spots.

Conus regius
Conidae

Common in the Caribbean, where it lives on rocks and detritus from a half a meter to 4.5 meters in depth. It preys on worms. It is from 4 to 4.5 centimeters high. Its name comes from the crown of tubercles that can be seen behind the last whorl. Color may vary.

Conus scalaris
Conidae

This species, which is not uncommon along the Pacific coast of Mexico south of Acapulco, has a spire with a distinctive graceful, ladder-like profile, and a slightly concave final whorl. It is from 3 to 6 centimeters high. It is white with chestnut spots.

Conus gloriamaris
Conidae

It was once considered the greatest malacological rarity, but is now found regularly in the Philippines. From 5 to 15 centimeters high, it has an especially graceful straight profile and a dense, fanciful and particularly elegant pattern.

Conus mediterraneus
Conidae

Common from the Mediterranean to the Cape Verde Islands in the Atlantic, and quite common in the midlittoral band at shallow depths, especially on rocky sea beds with algae. Its size ranges from 2 centimeters to, very rarely, 7 centimeters. Color is green-chestnut and quite variable.

Conus bullatus
Conidae

▶

Lives in the Pacific, from southern Japan to Polynesia and Hawaii, hidden beneath the sand of the infralittoral band. It is from 5 to 7 centimeters high, with the last whorl swollen and a flared aperture. Has a reddish pattern on white background. Rare.

◀ **Fusiturris undatiruga** (formerly Turris undatiruga)
Turridae

Beautiful deep water species that lives in the Mediterranean and along the Atlantic coast of Marocco. From 5 to 6.5 centimeters high, it is golden yellow with a chestnut band along the suture. Rather rare. Dense axial ribs obliquely intersect the spiral furrows.

Turris babylonia
Turridae

▶

The very slender form and the extremely long siphonal canal of this beautiful turrid, common in the mobile sea beds of the Indopacific, make it similar to a Fusinus. Its height varies from 6 to 10 centimeters. Each whorl has four carinae, with the third more prominent.

◀ **Turris auriculifera**
Turridae

Like other members of the family, this small turrid (its shell is 2.5 centimeters high), common in the shallow waters of the Indopacific, preys on small invertebrates by paralyzing them with an injection of poison, but is not dangerous to humans.

Thatcheria mirabilis - Japanese wonder shell
Turridae

▶

A masterpiece of the architectural ability of mollusks: light, fragile, from 6 to 10 centimeters high, it lives from Southern Japan to the Philippines at depths of 100 to 200 meters. The acute angle of the shoulder of the whorls gives the shell a pagoda-like appearance.

◀ **Raphitoma purpurea**
Turridae

Lives from Norway to the Mediterranean province, in the infralittoral band. It is reddish brown with a white or spotted basal band. An elegant network is formed by the intersection of the axial ribs with the spiral striae. It is from 20 to 25 millimeters high.

Mangelia vauquelini (formerly Cythara vauquelini)
Turridae

Has a glossy, yellow-white surface traversed by about ten axial ribs. A dark band crosses the suture among the whorls, while a reddish spot can be seen on the outer lip. It is from 10 to 12 millimeters high. Mediterranean province.

▶

151

Terebra succincta ▶
Terebridae

The prominent belt that traverses the whorls of the base distinguishes this small, slender shell (it is from 2 to 4 centimeters long). The small axial ribs of each whorl form a transverse network by intersecting the dense spiral striae. Indopacific.

Terebra subulata
Terebridae

Widespread species in the Indopacific. Lives in the sand in shallow water, where it uses its poison to prey on small invertebrates. An average of 13 centimeters long, it is cream-colored with three bands ◀ of square chestnut-colored markings.

Terebra dussumieri ▶
Terebridae

It is common on the mobile, shallow sea beds of the West Pacific, from Japan to Australia. From 6 to 10 centimeters high, the edge of each whorl is surmounted by a light band. The axial ribs are white, with chestnut intervals

◀ **Architectonica perspectiva**
Architettonidae

Shell with a conical profile and circular base: the very wide umbilicus makes it possible to see the beautiful internal structure. It is rather common in sandy infralittoral and circumlittoral sea beds in the Indopacific. From 3 to 4 centimeters in diameter.

Turbonilla lactea ▶
Pyramidellidae

Like the hundreds of other species in the Pyramidellidae family, this shell from the Mediterranean province has embryonal whorls surrounding an axis different from that of the spire. About 6-8 millimeters in height, with straight ribbing, white in color.

◀ **Chrisallida doliolum**
Piramidellidae

A strong magnifying glass is needed to fully appreciate the sculpture of this little shell less than 2.5 millimeters in size. Like all pyramidellids, it is a parasite of other mollusks and invertebrates, and lives in the Mediterranean. Has a swollen profile and prominent ribbing.

Acteon tornatilis
Acteonidae

Species common from the North Sea to the Mediterranean. It lives ▶ in shallow waters on sand and mud, as well as on tufts of sea lettuce in harbor areas. The shell is solid, from 15 to 25 millimeters high, from beige to rose colored, usually with a lighter band.

Scafander lignarius
Scafandridae

As is usually the case for opisthobranchs, it is not capable of retracting its entire body into the shell. It is a predator and lives in the Mediterranean on slimy sea beds a few dozen meters deep. The shell is from 6 to 8 centimeters high.

▶

◀ **Bulla striata**
Bullidae

Lives on sandy sea beds, especially Posidonia and Zostera meadows in the Mediterranean province. It feeds primarily on algae. The fragile, light shell is chestnut-colored, often with dark marbling.

Aplustrum amplustre
Bullidae

This rare shell comes from the sedimentary sea beds of the Indopacific. It is light, semi-transparent and has a design of rare elegance. Its bands of color, which vary in width, are orange and black on a cream background. Reaches 4 centimeters in length.

▶

◀ **Haminoea hydatis**
Hamineidae

The mollusks of this family (which includes about ninety species in tropical and temperate seas) have fragile, translucent shells which at least in part are permanently covered with the lobes of the mantle. From 8-11 millimeters long. Mediterranean.

Aplysia depilans - Sea hare
Aplysidae

The mollusk may reach 25 centimeters in length. Lives in shallow waters, especially where the algae on which it feeds grow most vigorously. The shell, which is completely internal, is reduced to a small translucent plate. It is 5 centimeters in diameter. Mediterranean.

▶

◀ **Clio pyramidata**
Cavolinidae

The species of this family of opisthobranchs live in plankton in the open sea. Their shells are completely internal. They can be found on detritus washed up on the beach or collected from the sea bed. Clio pyramidata is found in the Mediterranean. From 10-20 millimeters in length.

Ovatella firmini
Ellobiidae

The ellobiidae are lunged gastropods that live in a marine environment, but in the supralittoral band. There are 300 known species scattered throughout tropical and temperate regions. The one illustrated, 11 millimeters long, lives in Italy on pebbles in brackish pools.

▶

Siphonaria pectinata (formerly algesirae)
Siphonaridae

They look like limpets, with whom they share habitat and lifestyle, but the siphonarids, who have both gills and lungs, are very different from the evolutionary perspective. S. pectinata is 3.5 centimeters long and lives in the western Mediterranean province.

Nautilus pompilius - Nautilus
Nautilidae

Has a chambered shell that is marvelous to look at in cross section due to the perfection of its logarithmic spirals. Lives in the West Pacific at depths of over 50 meters, where it preys primarily on crustaceans. Its shell is from 10 to 20 centimeters long.

Spirula spirula
Spirulidae

A pelagic species, it is common in all seas of the world. It has a chambered shell like the nautilus, divided by septa traversed by a siphon, but the shell is almost completely inside the animal. Lives at depths of over 50 meters. Diameter is from 1.5 to 3.5 centimeters

Sepia officinalis - Cuttlefish
Sepiidae

What is commonly known as cuttlebone is the internal shell that testifies to the evolution of cephalopods: the plates in its spongy mass are the equivalent of the septa of Spirula. Lives in shallow waters in benthic areas in the Atlantic and Mediterranean.

Argonauta argo - Argonaut
Argonautidae

Pelagic species present in all warm and temperate seas. The shell that the female of this cephalopod builds with a specialized tentacle, is not a true shell, but a parchment-like structure used to protect its eggs. From 15-30 centimeters long.

Solemya togata - Robe awning clam
Solemyidae

This is a rather unevolved bivalve that lives in the sand in the infralittoral band, where it feeds on organic detritus. The foot acts as a piston to expel water from the mantle cavity. It lives in the Mediterranean. The shell is fragile and rare, 6 centimeters long.

Nucula nucleus
Nuculidae

Common from Norway to Natal and the Mediterranean, where it lives from 5 to 150 meters in depth, barely covered by silt or muddy or coarse sand. Its foot is better adapted to crawling than burying itself. The shell is one centimeter long.

Trisidos tortuosa
Arcidae

This arcid, about 6 centimeters long, that lives in the Indopacific on shallow, muddy sea beds, is distinguished by the fact that the line joining the two valves is not straight, but sinuous. Its color ranges from orange to pink.

Barbatia candida
Arcidae

Often found in fissures in the rock, where it then assumes the irregular form of the substratum. It is from 2.5 to 6.5 centimeters long, with a color that ranges from white to yellowish. The periostracum is brown. It lives in shallow waters from North Carolina to Brazil.

Arca zebra
Arcidae

This is a champion of mimicry: it lives anchored to the rock by its byssus, but allows itself to be covered by encrustations, and the beautiful zebra-striped shell becomes invisible. Has eyes along the mantle. Lives in the Caribbean, from 1 to 8 meters in depth.

Anadara corbuloides - Basket ark
Arcidae

Lives in the Mediterranean province from 30 to 100 meters deep. The back part of the shell is higher. The radial ribs (an average of 33) appear rough because they are crossed by the transverse sculpture. Length from 6 to 7 centimeters.

Scapharca inaequivalvis - Ark clam
Arcidae

Over recent years, this species, which originated in the Indopacific, has been the protagonist of a notorious invasion of the Mediterranean. Whitish in color, it is from 5 to 6.5 centimeters long, Lives buried in sand and mud in shallow waters.

Barbatia barbata - Bearded ark shell
Arcidae

Uses its byssus to anchor itself in colonies on reefs, rocks and sea fans. It is brown, with the periostracum covered by bristles that are more visible at the back end. Lives in the Mediterranean province, from a few meters to about 300 meters in depth. It is from 4-6 centimeters long.

Arca noae - Noah's ark
Arcidae

Found in the North Sea to the Mediterranean, and lives attached by its byssus to solid objects, from a few palms to about 100 meters in depth. The ventral margin has a byssal gape. From 7 to 9 centimeters long.

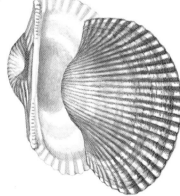

Glycymeris insubrica (formerly violascens) - Violet bittersweet ▶
Glycymeridae

Distinguished from similar species by its lighter, violet gray shell with light radial lines and a form that is generally somewhat square. From 4,5 to 6 centimeters long, it lives in shallow waters on mobile substrata in the Mediterranean province.

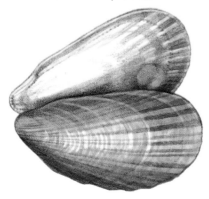

Lithofaga lithofaga - Date mussel ▶
Mytilidae

It uses the acid secretion of its mantle to dig tunnels in calcareous rock. For this reason, unlike other mytilids, it does not need to produce a byssus. The light shell, from 5 to 10 centimeters long, is covered by a brown periostracum.

◀ **Mytilus edulis** - Blue or common mussel
Mytilidae

This is a very widespread species, from Europe to the Americas, Japan, and the Arctic. It is more slender and less dark than the Mediterranean Mytilus galloprovincialis, but is highly variable. From 6 to 8 centimeters long.

◀ **Brachidontes variabilis**
Mytilidae

Is a member of the now numerous group of mollusks that have entered the Mediterranean through the Suez Canal. It is present along all the coasts of Africa. Lives in the midlittoral and infralittoral bands above the detrital layer. About 3 centimeters long.

Pteria hirundo - Winged oyster ▶
Pteriidae

Has a very distinctive form. Lives from southern England to the Mediterranean to the Azores, from a few meters deep, where it uses its byssus to attach to sea fans, to over 1000 meters deep on muddy sea beds. Up to 10 centimeters long.

◀ **Pinctada radiata**
Pteriidae

Lives attached to various supports, using its byssus, from 50 centimeters to dozens of meters deep, in all warm seas of the world, and entered the Mediterranean through the Suez Canal as early as the 19th century. Its diameter ranges from 6 to 10 centimeters.

Pinctada margaritifera - Pearl oyster ▶
Pteriidae

This Indopacific species is now cultivated for its pearls. It lives in the infralittoral band and beyond. Has an almost circular form and lamellae on the rayed sculpture. It is greenish gray with yellowish rays. Diameter up to 20 centimeters.

Malleus albus ▶
Malleidae

Found in shallow waters near coral reefs in the Indopacific. It has no byssus. The hammer-shaped shell (hence the Latin name) is completely white, adorned with lamellae, and rather fragile. Length from 10 to 20 centimeters.

Pinna nobilis - Fan mussel ▶
Pinnidae

The largest bivalve in the Mediterranean and one of the largest in the world: the shell can exceed 80 centimeters in length. Lives anchored and partially buried in Posidonia areas, where uncontrolled harvesting has decimated the populations.

◀ **Isognomon alatus**
Isognomonidae

Uses its byssus to anchor to the roots of mangroves in the Caribbean. It is a midlittoral species. The shell is quite flat and round. The ligament forms characteristic comb-like dimples. Diameter ranges from 2.5 to 11 centimeters.

Ostrea edulis - Flat oyster ▶
Ostreidae

A Celtic and Mediterranean province species, it has been cultivated since ancient Rome. It lives on various substrata in the midlittoral and infralittoral bands. The shape of the round shell varies depending on the substratum. Diameter from 7 to 10 centimeters.

◀ **Lima lima** - Spiny file shell
Limidae

Lives anchored by its byssus, in fissures in the rocks or among masses in the infralittoral band, in all warm seas in the world, including the Mediterranean. Has a ham form with short spines on 18-22 radial ribs. From 4 to 5 centimeters long.

Neopycnodonte cochlear ▶
Gryphaeidae

A deep water species (from 30 to over 1000 meters), it grows by adhering to various solid surfaces, including the thorns of sea urchins, and takes many different forms. In general the top valve (cover) is set into the other one (cup). Cosmopolitan. Reaches 8.5 centimeters in size.

◀ **Lopha cristagalli**
Ostreidae

The edges of the valves have 4-8 large folds at acute angles that resemble a rooster's crest. Lives attached to rocks and corals, using the aid of special anchoring spines, in the infralittoral band. It is an Indopacific species with a diameter of up to 9 centimeters.

Pecten maximus Great scallop
Pettinidae

▶

Lives in the Atlantic from Norway to the Canaries, on sandy sea beds from shallow waters to 200 meters in depth. Prized in fish markets (Coquille de Saint-Jacques). Has a series of ocelli on the edge of the mantle. About 15 centimeters in diameter.

◀ **Pecten jacobaeus -** Common scallop
Pettinidae

Chlamys rubida
Pectinidae

Distinguished from Pecten maximus by the edges of the shell with the angular rather than rounded crests, and by the absence of prominent growth lines. Lives in the Mediterranean on sandy sea beds from 25 to 190 meters deep. 15 centimeters in diameter.

Circular in form, with a diameter that rarely exceeds 6 centimeters, it lives on rocky or pebbly sea beds along the western coasts of North America, from Alaska to Monterey, from the low tide mark to about 180 meters deep. It is often covered with sponges from the genera Myxilla and Mycale, which help to camouflage it.

▶

◀ **Chlamys varia -** Variegated scallop
Pettinidae

Highly variable in color, from white to blackish, including yellow, green, red, marbled or plain colored. Uses its byssus to anchor to hard substrata from a few meters to over 100 meters deep. Diameter from 4-5 centimeters. Mediterranean, Atlantic and North Sea.

Chlamys pesfelis - Cat's paw scallop
Pettinidae

▶

The shell is higher than it is wide, and may be from 5 to 7 centimeters in size. The upper valve has 8 large radial ribs. The prominent knobs near the edge resemble a cat's paw. Lives in the Atlantic and Mediterranean, from 10 to 230 meters in depth.

◀ **Nodipecten nodosus** (formerly Chlamys nodosus)
Pettinidae

The color varies from orange to red purple, with a diameter from 6 to 12 centimeters. There are 7 or 8 ribs and the large knobs are hollow. It lives on coarse sand or detritus, from 10 to 50 meters deep, from North Carolina to Brazil.

Placopecten magellanicus (formerly Chlamys magellanicus)
Pettinidae

▶

It is circular, and the right valve (light) is flatter than the left (reddish). It is 5 to 20 centimeters in diameter. It is sold on fish markets in America. Lives from the Gulf of Saint Lawrence to North Carolina, on sand or shingles, from 18-122 meters deep.

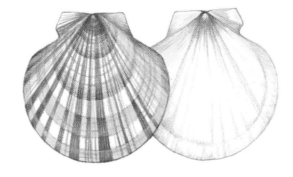

Amusium japonicus
Pettinidae

▶

Orbicular and fragile, it is noteworthy for the color of the upper valve, a mahogany red that contrasts with the straw yellow of the edge of the white lower valve. Lives in Japan, on sand and mud, in the infralittoral band. About 11 centimeters in diameter.

Spondylus princeps
Spondilidae

◀

It adheres to reefs with the right valve, while the free left valve has radial ribs adorned by spectacular paddle-shaped spines up to 3.5 centimeters long. Lives from California to Peru in shallow waters. Up to 13 centimeters in diameter.

Spondylus gaederopus - Thorny oyster
Spondylidae

▶

A red sponge, Crambe crambe, often hides its upper valve, while the other one adheres to the reef. Spiny appendages are more or less developed. Infralittoral. Diameter from 8-13.5 centimeters. Mediterranean and Senegalese provinces.

Anomia ephippium - Saddle oyster
Anomiidae

◀

Extremely variable, it shapes itself to the substratum to which it adheres. The lower valve has a hole through which the byssus runs. Up to 7 centimeters in diameter. Lives anywhere, down to 150 meters deep, from Norway to the Mediterranean to Ghana.

Myrtea spinifera
Lucinidae

▶

Widespread species, from North America to Europe to Ceylon. Lives on muddy sea beds from the infralittoral band to 900 meters deep. Dull gray or ivory colored, up to 2.5 centimeters in diameter. The back dorsal edge has a series of teeth.

Loripes lacteus
Lucinidae

◀

Has a lenticular form, is pure white, diameter from 2 to 2.4 centimeters. Gathered for food. Lives from England to Senegal and in the Mediterranean. Found on various types of sea beds to 100 meters in depth, as well as in brackish lagoons.

Carditamera floridana
Carditidae

▶

Very robust shell, white or grayish, with prominent radial ribs with beading traversed by chestnut spots, forming concentric bands. Lives on sandy or muddy sea beds from 1 to 7.5 meters deep, from southern Florida to Mexico.

Cardita crassicosta
Carditidae

▶

Has a square shape, with beautiful lamellae with wider tips on the radial ribs. The color is variable: white, yellow, pink and red. Lives at shallow depths, using its byssus to anchor to the substratum, in the Indopacific and Australia.

Chama gryphoides
Chamidae

▶

Chamids have one valve, used to adhere to the substratum, which is very concave, and another flat one used as a cover. This species lives in the Atlantic, Mediterranean and Red Sea, from shallow to very deep waters. Reaches 2.8 centimeters in length.

◀ ### Cardita calcyculata
Carditidae

Oblong, distended at the back, white with pink or chestnut spots. The ventral margin is sinuous. It is from 2 to 2.3 centimeters long. Lives in the Portuguese Atlantic and the Mediterranean in the sublittoral band to over 200 meters in depth.

Astarte fusca
Astartidae

▶

Thick shell with about 15 concentric furrows, either brown or chestnut. Lives on muddy-detrital sea beds in the Mediterranean and Portuguese Atlantic to the Canary Islands, at depths between 30 and 80 meters. Diameter from 2 to 2.4 centimeters.

◀ ### Gonilia calliglypta
Astartidae

Small, rare and little known, it has a distinctive frond-like ornamentation on the valves. Lives in the circumlittoral band in the Mediterranean province, on sandy, slimy and coral sea beds with abundant detritus. Its diameter ranges from 3 to 5 millimeters.

◀ ### Acanthocardia tuberculata - Red nose cockle
Cardiidae

A Mediterranean and Celtic species that lives on fine or coarse sand, including oarweed sea beds, from shallow waters to about 100 meters deep. Diameter from 5 to 8 centimeters. Has from 19 to 24 rounded ribs, which are knobby toward the front.

Acanthocardia aculeata - Spiny cockle
Cardiidae

▶

The approximately twenty radial ribs that adorn the shell have pointed tubercles, more evident on the back side and along the margins. Lives in the Mediterranean and Celtic provinces on sandy or muddy infralittoral sea beds. Diameter from 6 to 10 centimeters.

Laevicardium crassum
Cardiidae

▶

Has a light shell, 2.5-2.8 centimeters in size, that is a cream color, often with red spots. Lives in the circumlittoral band on detrital sea beds, but has been found as deep as 2000 meters. Common in Mediterranean, Senegalese, Celtic and Boreal provinces.

◀ **Corculum cardissa**
Cardiidae

Lives in the midlittoral band on mobile sea beds near coral formations in the Indopacific, and adheres to the substratum with a small byssus. Form is flattened from front to back. Yellow with little red spots. 5 centimeters in diameter.

Cerastoderma edule - Common edible cockle
Cardiidae

▶

A polymorph species that can adapt to highly diverse salinity conditions, from extremely salty bodies of water to almost freshwater. Lives in shallow waters on sand or mud from the Arctic to Senegal and in the Mediterranean to the Caspian. Reaches 5 centimeters in size.

◀ **Cardium costatum**
Cardiidae

Large cardiid whose area is limited to the Senegalese province. The valves are light, fragile and white, 10 centimeters in diameter. Its sculpture consists of about twenty high ribs with a triangular cross-section. Lives on mobile circumlittoral sea beds.

Tridacna squamosa
Tridacnidae

▶

Not the largest, but perhaps the most elegant of the small Tridacnidae family. It is adorned with 5 or 6 radial ribs with large, paddle-shaped appendages. Reaches 30 centimeters in length. Lives among corals in the Indopacific.

◀ **Hippopus hippopus**
Tridacnidae

This tridacnid with a square profile may be up to 40 centimeters in length. It lives in coral sands near the reef, to a depth of 5 or 6 meters, in the Indopacific. It is common where it is not overharvested.

Mactra corallina - Trough shell
Mactridae

▶

Is washed up by the rough sea in immense quantities on the sandy coasts of its vast territory, running from Norway to Senegal to the Mediterranean. Its white color is often a background for patterns of dark lines. Its diameter is from 4.5 to 6 centimeters.

Lutraria lutraria - Otter shell
Mactridae

The two valves are somewhat open at the ends. It is whitish in color, with a brownish periostracum. It is from 11 to 12 centimeters in size. Lives on mobile sea beds from the sublittoral band to about 50 meters in depth, from Norway to Guinea to the Mediterranean.

Donacilla cornea - Wedge shell
Mesodesmatidae

Looks like a donacid, but the inside marginal edge is smooth, not crenulated. Lives in infralittoral sand in the Celtic and Mediterranean provinces. From 1.8 to 2.4 centimeters long and very robust, with a glossy outer surface. Yellow with lighter tones.

Solen marginatus - Yellow razor clam
Solenidae

Has almost straight edges and a characteristic single transverse furrow near the front edge, narrowing on the ventral side. An average of 12.5 centimeters long. Sandy infralittoral and circumlittoral sea beds from Norway to Angola to the Mediterranean.

Ensis ensis - Razor clam
Cultellidae

Has a arcuate, rounded form at the ends. It is yellow-cream in color, with dark streaks. The maximum length is 16 centimeters. Lives from the Arctic to Morocco and the Mediterranean, on fine or slimy sand, up to about 90 meters deep.

Tellina radiata
Tellinidae

In America it is known as the sunrise tellin, due to the pink rays on the glossy surface that look like a sunrise. Lives from Florida to the coast of South America, in sand at depths of from 1.5 to 15 meters. From 5 to 11 centimeters long.

Tellina pulchella - Red tellin
Tellinidae

The back portion is visibly beaked and the ventral margin is a bit sinuous toward the beak. Pink with light radial lines. From 2 to 3.2 centimeters long. Lives buried deep in sublittoral sands of the Mediterranean.

Tellina pharaonis
Tellinidae

It is fragile, with a singular appearance, as the cavities of the back margins give it a beaked form. It is a fleshy red color, with concentric white or yellowish bands. Lives in Australia on sandy sea beds at modest depths.

Tellina incarnata - Fleshy tellin
Tellinidae

▶

Has a compressed form and oval profile in the front portion, while the back is carinate. It is a fleshy orange color that is brighter near the umbones. Lives on the mobile sea beds of the Mediterranean, from the infralittoral band to 60 meters deep.

◀ **Tellina crassa**
Tellinidae

Lives from Sweden to Senegal on coarse or muddy-detrital sand from the infralittoral band to 150 meters deep, and also at the western tip of the Mediterranean. Robust shell from 4 to 7 centimeters long. Light, with little orange spots.

Strigilla carnaria
Tellinidae

▶

The oblique sculpture created by the rough little ribs gives it the Latin name for rasp. It is almost circular in form, and pink in color. It lives in the sand (from 3 to 37 meters deep) from Florida to Brazil. From 1.9 to 2.8 centimeters in size.

◀ **Macoma balthica**
Tellinidae

This little cockle, very common in the seas of northwest Europe, lives in sand or mud from a few centimeters to 14 meters deep. It is from 2 to 3,5 centimeters long, and the internal portion is a brighter pink than the outside.

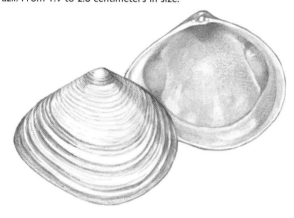

Gastrana fragilis
Tellinidae

▶

The largest specimens reach 4.5 centimeters in length. It is dirty white, with dense concentric lines covering the surface. Lives from the Arctic to Morocco and the Mediterranean, on muddy detrital sea beds in the infralittoral and circumlittoral bands.

◀ **Scrobicularia plana** - Scrobicularia
Scrobiculariidae

This species prefers mud and brackish waters and lives in very sheltered inlets and the mouths of rivers, on shallow sea beds in the Celtic and Mediterranean provinces. The surface is grayish, traversed by growth lines. From 4 to 5.5 centimeters long.

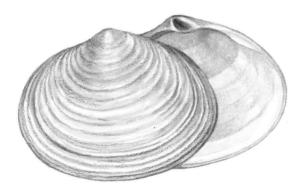

Solecurtus scopola (formerly strigilatus) - Solecurtus clam
Solecurtidae

▶

Has almost parallel margins and a rectangular appearance. Oblique striae adorn the pink surface, with two lighter radial bands. From 7-8 centimeters in length. Lives in fine sand in the Mediterranean province, to depths of 150 meters.

Pharus legumen - Bean solen
Solecurtidae

▶

Has a fragile shell in the form of a pod, yellowish or flesh-colored. A thin, deciduous epidermis often protrudes at the edges of the valves. From 5 to 6 centimeters long, it lives along the Iberian coasts and in the Mediterranean, from 10 to 100 meters in depth.

◀ **Donax variabilis**
Donacidae

Quite abundant in the tidal areas of sandy North American beaches, from New York to northern Mexico. From 13 to 25 millimeters long, its color varies greatly, with radial and concentric bands that may be pink, violet, yellow, blue or orange.

Donax trunculus - Coquina
Donacidae

▶

Lives buried in sandy and muddy sea beds in shallow waters in the Mediterranean, where it is one of the most common species. In some areas it can even be found in fish markets. It is yellowish in color, with lighter rays. Length varies from 2 to 4 centimeters.

◀ **Arctica islandica**
Arcticidae

This Atlantic species lives along the coasts of western Europe, Iceland and North America (from Newfoundland to North Carolina), on muddy sand, from 9 to 260 meters deep. Diameter from 5 to 12 centimeters. Its color runs from dark olive to black.

Glossus humanus
Glossidae

▶

The twisted, spiraling umbones are a characteristic of this globular, light shell. Lives in the Mediterranean, Celtic and Boreal provinces, including North America, from 7 to over 3500 meters deep, on sand and mud. From 7-8 centimeters in diameter.

◀ **Venus verrucosa -** Sea truffle or warty Venus
Veneridae

Prized by gourmets, it lives on various sea beds (sand, sandy-rocky) in the western Atlantic and the Mediterranean, from shallow waters to depths of about 100 meters. Yellowish gray in color, from 4 to 7 centimeters in diameter.

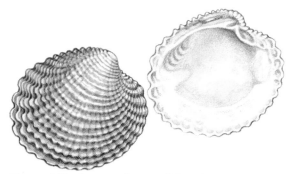

Tapes philippinarum - Japanese littleneck
Veneridae

▶

It has spread from East Asia to Europe and America and has colonized Venice's lagoon. Subject to intensive cultivation. From 4 to 6.5 centimeters long, it prefers sea beds of muddy sand in sheltered inlets right below the low tide mark.

Tapes litteratus
Veneridae ►

The network of lines that intersect at acute angles on the surface of this venerid resemble an alphabet, giving it its name. From 4 to 9 centimeters long, it is common on shallow sea beds in the Indopacific, especially in the Philippines.

Pitar lupanarius
Veneridae ◄

Two series of spines rising from the concentric sculpture of the shell distinguish these species. From 5 to 8 centimeters long, it lives in infralittoral sands to 20 meters deep in the Pacific, from southern California to Peru.

Mercenaria mercenaria
Veneridae ►

Originally from the Atlantic coast of North America, it was introduced to California for its commercial value. The inside of the valves has a purple spot. About 10 centimeters long, it lives in sand and mud to a depth of 15 meters.

Lioconcha castrensis
Veneridae ◄

Its tent-shaped decoration, brown or reddish on an ivory surface, suggests a military camp (castrum in Latin). It is 4 centimeters long, solid, and common in coral sands near coral reefs in the Indopacific.

Irus irus
Veneridae ►

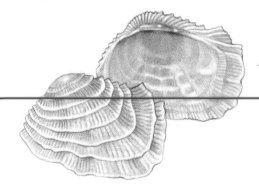

The form varies depending on the cavity in the rock in which it lives. From 2 to 2.3 centimeters long, it is adorned with concentric laminae and fine radial striae. Lives on solid infralittoral substrata in Celtic, Mediterranean and Senegalese provinces.

Chamelea gallina - Common clam
Veneridae ◄

Very important for food, this venerid lives on sandy sea beds in the Mediterranean province, at shallow depths. Excessive harvesting has reduced populations in areas where it was extremely abundant. It may reach 45 millimeters in diameter.

Callista chione - Callista venus shell
Veneridae ►

Beautiful robust shell, from 6 to 11 centimeters long, with a very glossy surface, red-brown tending to pink. Harvested for food. Lives on sand to 200 meters deep in Celtic and Mediterranea provinces.

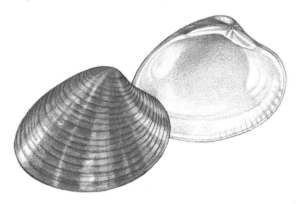

Bassina disiecta
Veneridae

▶

Characterized by its rich ornamentation of thin, rather fragile laminae. It is rosy white in color. Reaches 6.4 centimeters in length. Lives in the infralittoral band at shallow depths, in muddy sand in southern Australia.

◀ **Petricola lithofaga**
Petricolidae

Lives in cavities that it digs in rocks or other hard substrata, or in fissures it finds in the infralittoral band. A fragile, whitish shell, truncated in front and elongated in back. From 1.5 to 2.6 centimeters long. Mediterranean and Celtic provinces.

Mya arenaria
Myidae

▶

Oval form, thin valves open at the two ends, a chalky white color. From 2.5 to 14 centimeters long. An important food species, it lives in sand and mud from the tide mark to 70 meters deep. North Atlantic and California.

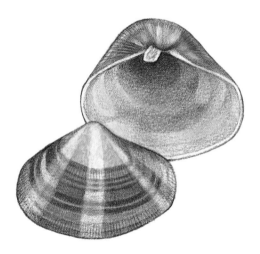

◀ **Corbula gibba**
Corbulidae

Globular shell with a smaller right valve that fits into the left valve. From 10 to 16 millimeters long. Lives in sand and mud, from the littoral band to 2000 meters deep. Celtic, Mediterranean, Senegalese and Boreal provinces.

Panopea generosa
Iatellidae

▶

The valves of this large shell (from 9 to 23 centimeters) touch only at the umbo and do not enclose the whole mollusk, which may weigh 3.5 kilos. Lives buried in the mud in tranquil, shallow inlets from Alaska to Mexico.

◀ **Hiatella arctica**
Iatellidae

Widespread throughout the northern hemisphere, it lives in holes that it digs in soft rock, or in fissures, from a few centimeters to abyssal depths. Small, robust, from 17 to 25 millimeters long. The left valve is smaller than the right one

Pholas dactylus
Pholadidae

Digs tunnels up to 25 centimeters long in the rock, but also in other substrata, provided they are hard enough. The shell is white, fragile, open, and from 8 to 11 centimeters long. Lives in the infralittoral band from Norway to Cape Verde and in the Mediterranean.

▶

Teredo navalis - Ship-worm
Teredinidae

The animal has the form of a worm and lives in tunnels that it digs in wood of any kind, causing damage to boats and structures. The shell is reduced to two anterior plates (about 6 millimeters) and two blades that protect the siphons. The tube can be longer than 50 centimeters. Cosmopolitan.

Cuspidaria rostrata
Cuspidariidae

The rostrum that gives it its name is an open, tubular extension that protects the siphons. The fragile white shell with cream-colored periostracum is 2-3 centimeters in length. Lives on muddy and clayey sea beds from 30 meters in depth and beyond. Atlantic and Mediterranean.

Dentalium dentalis
Dentaliidae

The shell, fragile-looking and quite varied in color (from white to gray to rose), has 10 thin, rounded ribs in the apical portion, while the aperture is circular. Lives in the Mediterranean, from 1 to 200 meters in depth.

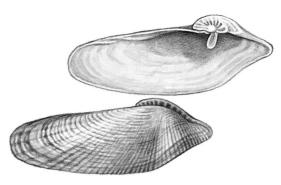

◀ **Cyrtopleura costata**
Pholadidae

Americans call it the angel wing, due to the lightness and elegance of its pure white shell, from 10 to 20 centimeters long. Lives buried in muddy sand from the tidal line to 18 meters deep, from Massachusetts to Brazil.

▶

◀ **Penicillus australis**
Clavagellidae

The two valves are reduced to tiny open plates, while the body is protected through the construction of a calcareous shell. Lives buried in sand in shallow water. The tube is about 20 centimeters long. Indopacific.

◀ **Dentalium elephantinum**
Dentaliidae

This is the most showy shell in the entire class of scaphopods. Bright green ringed with black, with very prominent ribs. It is 7 centimeters long. Lives in the Indopacific, from the Philippines to Australia, in sandy sea beds about 30 meters deep.

▶

◀ **Cadulus jeffreysi**
Siphonodentaliidae

Tiny, glossy, translucent shell, 3 to 4 millimeters in length. Has a small swelling in the middle-anterior portion and a thickening to the back. Lives in the circumlittoral band, generally on mud, in Mediterranean, Celtic and Boreal provinces.

167

168 - This large Hyotissa hyotis from the Indopacific, which lives in coral formations from the tidal zone to about twenty meters deep, is not a true oyster. It reaches 20 centimeters in diameter. The specimen photographed is camouflaged by a sponge on its shell.

PHOTOGRAPHIC CREDITS